NARRATIVE POEMS

NARRATIVE POEMS

SELECTED BY

E. W. PARKER, M.C.

LONGMANS, GREEN AND CO.

LONDON · NEW YORK · TORONTO

LONGMANS, GREEN AND CO. LTD.
OF PATERNOSTER ROW
43 ALBERT DRIVE, LONDON, S.W.19
NICOL ROAD, BOMBAY
17 CHITTARANJAN AVENUE, CALCUTTA
36A MOUNT ROAD, MADRAS

LONGMANS, GREEN AND CO.
55 FIFTH AVENUE, NEW YORK, 3

LONGMANS, GREEN AND CO.
215 VICTORIA STREET, TORONTO, 1

First published 1946

CODE NUMBER: 69139

PRINTED IN GREAT BRITAIN BY
NORTHUMBERLAND PRESS LIMITED
GATESHEAD ON TYNE

FOREWORD

HERE is a collection of tales in verse, narrated by poets both of our own time and of the past who all have one thing in common—they are young enough in heart to know how to awaken an immediate response in the hearts of boys and girls of to-day. The contents vary from stories arousing merry laughter to tales of gallant adventure by land and sea. Many of the poems have been written by modern poets, while others have enchanted successive generations of readers whose pulses they have quickened.

While the poets both old and new are thus weaving their magic spell, they will not fail to arouse that latent love of poetry common to all—a love that will grow with the years that bring experience and maturity. When those who now respond to the poet's mood venture forth in their turn to encounter the tasks of the future, it may be that the noble songs of the poets will then ring in their ears, stirring them to face with undaunted courage and merry hearts the adventure of living.

E.W.P.

ACKNOWLEDGMENTS

I HAVE great pleasure in recording my grateful thanks to Dr. P. Gurrey who has once again given me the benefit of his advice and experience.

My thanks are also due to the owners of the copyright poems and versions of older poems that are reprinted in this collection:

Messrs. Edward Arnold & Co. for " The Ballad of Richard Peake " from *Ballads of the Fleet* by Lord Rennell of Rodd; Mrs. Binyon for " Stamford Bridge " and " John Winter " by Laurence Binyon from *Collected Poems* published by Messrs. Macmillan & Co. Ltd.; The Clarendon Press Ltd. for " Jock o' the Side ", " Thomas Rymer ", " Hynd Horn " and " The Daemon Lover " from *The Oxford Book of Ballads* edited by Sir Arthur Quiller-Couch, and for stanzas from " Eros and Psyche " from *The Poetical Works of Robert Bridges*; Mr. Walter de la Mare and Messrs. Constable & Co. Ltd. for " The O'M-O-R-E " from *Poems 1919-1934*, and " Off the Ground " and " Sam's Three Wishes " from *Peacock Pie*; Mr. W. W. Gibson and Messrs. Macmillan & Co. Ltd. for " Flannan Isle " from *Collected Poems 1905-1925*; Miss Nancy McIntosh and Messrs. Macmillan & Co. Ltd. for " The Yarn of the *Nancy Bell* " from *Bab Ballads* by Sir W. S. Gilbert; Mr. John Masefield, Messrs. William Heinemann Ltd. and The Macmillan Company of Canada for extracts from " Reynard the Fox "; the author's representatives, Messrs. Methuen & Co. Ltd. and The Macmillan Company of Canada for " The Ballad of the Clampherdown " from *Barrack Room Ballads* by Rudyard Kipling; Mr. Alfred Noyes and Messrs. William Blackwood & Sons Ltd. for the extract from " A Knight of the Ocean-sea " from *Collected Poems, Volume 3*; Mr. E. V. Rieu and Messrs. Methuen & Co. Ltd. for " The Whale " from *Cuckoo Calling*; and Messrs. Martin Secker & Warburg Ltd. for " Miss Thompson Goes Shopping " from *The Buzzards* by Martin Armstrong.

CONTENTS

vii

CONTENTS

THE O'-M-O-R-E

'Tis years fourscore
Since Rory O'More—
He and his brothers three,
Patrick, Seumas, and Timothy Tim,
With the Pole Star shining free,
Sailed with the sail, and an oar for a rudder,
Bound for an Unknown Sea.

Bound for that Unknown Sea forlore
Mariners many have sailed before;
Into the evening mist they swing,
Daring whatever the dark may bring;
And so went Timothy, Seumas, and Pat,
Each with a sprig of yew in his hat,
And so sailed Rory O'More.

Sailed. . . . But a wind come out of a cloud,
Piping shrill and long and loud,
Smote on their boat as they did float,
Stretched their cloaks on the stoop o' the wave,
Violet, azure and green-grass-green,
And Rory's of scarlet brave;
Tossed them adrift on the foam of the main,
Bowed on them, fawned on them, bowed again;
Roared them to slumber, deep, serene,
Made of their sail their shroud. . . .

Yet still 'tis whispered, and still 'tis said
That fishermen, weary and sore bestead,

Hauling their nets on the watery deep,
Numb with cold and half asleep,
Will lift their eyes from the spray and spy
Ghosts in the glint of the moon pass by—
Phantoms four of the name of O'More,
Lifting their heads they see—
Patrick, Seumas, and Timothy Tim,
And Rory walking free.
Arm in arm where the petrels skim
Over the billow's hissing brim,
Swinging their feet through the surges they go,
Four jolly ghosts in a glimmering row,
Four abreast, and nodding their heads,
Walking the waves these ghostly lads,
Haunting the wind with their voices four,
Timothy, Patrick, Seumas, and Ror—
Rory O'More.

Striding the sea-drifts leagues from shore,
Ghosts of his brothers and Rory O'More
Fishermen white
In that haze of light,
Dazed with its radiance, see,
And sigh in a breath,
Their beards beneath,
"See! there! the O'-M-O-R-E!
We have seen the O'-M-O-R-E!"

WALTER DE LA MARE

THE WHALE

A whale of the cachalot sort
  Came up from the depths with a snort,
And lifting his tail like a thundering flail
  Belaboured the sea in his sport.
  The flying-fish shuddered in fright
  And the porpoises paled at the sight
Of the foam and commotion he made in the ocean
  A league to the left and the right.

A volcano looked down on the bay
  And smoked in a satisfied way:
The fumes of his fire rose up like a spire—
  Leviathan paused in his play.
  And he said with a watery sigh,
  " The monster is greater than I!
How I envy this mountain whose spout is a fountain
  That reaches the roof of the sky! "

With a feeling akin to chagrin
  He sounded and sank from the scene;
And he killed a great squid (in his anger he did)
  With an eye like a porridge tureen.
  Then he turned his square nose to the Pole,
  His southern and ultimate goal,
And brooding on slaughter he sped through the water
  With never a word to a soul.

And he came to the country of ice
  And circled the continent twice.

"He is missing his meals," cried the motherly seals;
    While the penguins were free with advice.
    Till at length upon Enderby Deep,
    Where the snow-laden hurricanes sweep,
With the Antarctic billows for bedding and pillows
    He rocked in a merciful sleep.

    He had slept on his passionate pride
    For the ebb and the flood of a tide,
When a maidenly whale with a tapering tail
    Rose up from the sea at his side.
    She gave him a whimsical look,
    And a touch of her delicate fluke,
And fled from his waking with tender heart quaking
    In fear of rebuff or rebuke.

    But as one who awakes from a swoon
    To the sound of a magical tune
He was caught by the gleam of her silvery beam
    In the diamond light of the moon;
    And from out of the slough of despond,
    To the edge of the sea and beyond,
Where the Aurora lingers with flickering fingers,
    He followed her foolish and fond.

    And he sang her a sea serenade:
    "My queen, be no longer afraid.
I will make you a home in the heart of the foam,
    O lovely and lovable maid!"
    And the candles of night were put out
    By Dawn, the dispeller of doubt,
As the maid oceanic, forgetting her panic,
    Replied, with a feathery spout:

"O cachalot, king of the blue,
  I will swim with you loyal and true.
In weal or in woe, wheresoever you go,
  I will dive with no other than you.
  Where the Kraken lies secretly curled,
  Where the hissing harpoon may be hurled,
In battle and thunder, above seas or under,
  I am yours to the ends of the world!"

So he swam by the side of his queen
  Conversing of days that had been,
And he spoke in a gay and a casual way
  Of the *little* volcano he'd seen.
  And she heard with the ghost of a smile,
  But a heart that was empty of guile,
As they journeyed together through fair and foul
    weather,
  By ice-floe and iceberg and isle.

E. V. RIEU

THE WRAGGLE TAGGLE GIPSIES

There were three gipsies a-come to my door,
  And downstairs ran this a-lady, O!
One sang high, and another sang low,
  And the other sang, Bonny, bonny Biscay, O!

Then she pulled off her silk-finished gown
  And put on hose of leather, O!
The ragged, ragged rags about our door—
  She's gone with the wraggle taggle gipsies, O!

It was late last night, when my lord came home,
Enquiring for his a-lady, O!
The servants said, on every hand:
" She's gone with the wraggle taggle gipsies, O! "

" O saddle to me my milk-white steed.
Go and fetch me my pony, O!
That I may ride and seek my bride,
Who is gone with the wraggle taggle gipsies, O! "

O he rode high and he rode low,
He rode through woods and copses too,
Until he came to an open field,
And there he espied his a-lady, O!

" What makes you leave your house and land?
What makes you leave your money, O?
What makes you leave your new-wedded lord:
To go with the wraggle taggle gipsies, O? "

" What care I for my house and my land?
What care I for my money, O?
What care I for my new-wedded lord?
I'm off with the wraggle taggle gipsies, O! "

" Last night you slept on a goose-feather bed,
With the sheet turned down so bravely, O!
And to-night you'll sleep in a cold open field,
Along with the wraggle taggle gipsies, O! "

" What care I for a goose-feather bed,
With the sheet turned down so bravely, O?
For to-night I shall sleep in a cold open field,
Along with the wraggle taggle gipsies, O! "

ANONYMOUS

THE WHITE SHIP

HENRY I OF ENGLAND—NOVEMBER 25, 1120

By none but me can the tale be told,
The butcher of Rouen, poor Berold.
    (Lands are swayed by a King on a throne.)
'Twas a royal train put forth to sea,
Yet the tale can be told by none but me.
    (The sea hath no King but God alone.)

King Henry held it as life's whole gain
That after his death his son should reign.

'Twas so in my youth I heard men say
And my old age calls it back to-day.

King Henry of England's realm was he,
And Henry Duke of Normandy.

The times had changed when on the coast
" Clerkly Harry " was all his boast.

Of ruthless strokes full many a one
He struck to crown himself and his son,
And his elder brother's eyes were gone.

And when to the chase his court would crowd,
The poor flung ploughshares on his road,
And shrieked " Our cry is from King to God! "

But the chief of the English land
Had knelt and kissed the Prince's hand.

And next with his son he sailed to France
To claim the Norman allegiance.

And every baron in Normandy
Had taken the oath of fealty.

'Twas sworn and sealed, and the day had come
When the King and the Prince might journey home.

. . . .

The King set sail with the eve's south wind,
And soon he left that coast behind.

The Prince and all his, a princely show,
Remained in the good White Ship to go.

With noble knights and with ladies fair,
With courtiers and sailors gathered there,
Three hundred living souls we were:

And I, Berold, was the meanest hind
In all that train to the Prince assign'd.

And now he cried: "Bring wine from below;
Let the sailors revel ere yet they row:

"Our speed shall o'ertake my father's flight
Though we sail from the harbour at midnight."

The rowers made good cheer without check;
The lords and ladies obeyed his beck;
The night was light, and they danced on the deck.

Swifter and swifter the White Ship sped
Till she flew as the spirit flies from the dead:

8

As white as a lily glimmered she
Like a ship's fair ghost upon the sea.

And the Prince cried, " Friends, 'tis the hour to sing!
Is a songbird's course so swift on the wing? "

And under the winter stars' still throng,
From brown throats, white throats, merry and strong,
The knights and the ladies raised a song.

A song,—nay, a shriek that rent the sky,
That leaped o'er the deep!—the grievous cry
Of three hundred living that now must die.

An instant shriek that sprang to the shock
As the ship's keel felt the sunken rock.

'Tis said that afar—a shrill strange sigh—
The King's ships heard it and knew not why.

Pale Fitz-Stephen stood by the helm
'Mid all those folk that the waves must whelm.

A great King's heir for the waves to whelm,
And the helpless pilot pale at the helm!

The ship was eager and sucked athirst,
By the steady stab of the sharp reef pierc'd.

And like the moil round a sinking cup
The waters against her crowded up!

A moment the pilot's senses spin,—
The next he snatched the Prince 'mid the din,
Cut the boat loose, and the youth leaped in.

A few friends leaped with him, standing near.
" Row! the sea's smooth and the night is clear! "

" What! none to be saved but these and I? "
" Row, row as you'd live!   All here must die! "

Out of the churn of the choking ship,
Which the gulf grapples and the waves strip,
They struck with the strained oars' flash and dip.

'Twas then o'er the splitting bulwarks' brim
The Prince's sister screamed to him.

He gazed aloft, still rowing apace,
And through the whirled surf he knew her face.

To the toppling decks clave one and all
As a fly cleaves to a chamber-wall.

I, Berold, was clinging anear;
I prayed for myself and quaked with fear,
But I saw his eyes as he looked at her.

He knew her face and he heard her cry,
And he said, " Put back! she must not die! "

And back with the current's force they reel
Like a leaf that's drawn to a water-wheel.

'Neath the ship's travail they scarce might float,
But he rose and stood in the rocking boat.

Low the poor ship leaned on the tide:
O'er the naked keel as she best might slide,
The sister toiled to the brother's side.

He reached an oar to her from below,
And stiffened his arms to clutch her so.

But now from the ship some spied the boat,
And " Saved! " was the cry from many a throat.

And down to the boat they leaped and fell:
It turned as a bucket turns in a well,
And nothing was there but the surge and swell.

The Prince that was and the King to come,
There in an instant gone to his doom,

Despite of all England's bended knee
And maugre the Norman fealty!

He was a Prince of lust and pride;
He showed no grace till the hour he died.

When he should be King, he oft would vow,
He'd yoke the peasant to his own plough.
O'er him the ships score their furrows now.

God only knows where his soul did wake,
But I saw him die for his sister's sake.

By none but me can the tale be told,
The butcher of Rouen, poor Berold.
   (*Lands are swayed by a King on a throne.*)
'Twas a royal train put forth to sea,
Yet the tale can be told by none but me.
   (*The sea hath no King but God alone.*)

DANTE GABRIEL ROSSETTI

HEATHER ALE

From the bonny bells of heather
  They brewed a drink long-syne,
Was sweeter far than honey,
  Was stronger far than wine.
They brewed it and they drank it,
  And lay in a blessed swound
For days and days together
  In their dwellings underground.

There rose a king in Scotland,
  A fell man to his foes,
He smote the Picts in battle,
  He hunted them like roes.
Over miles of the red mountain
  He hunted as they fled,
And strewed the dwarfish bodies
  Of the dying and the dead.

Summer came in the country,
  Red was the heather bell;
But the manner of the brewing
  Was none alive to tell.
In graves that were like children's
  On many a mountain head,
The Brewsters of the Heather
  Lay numbered with the dead.

The king in the red moorland
  Rode on a summer's day;
And the bees hummed, and the curlews
  Cried beside the way.

The king rode, and was angry,
    Black was his brow and pale,
To rule in a land of heather
    And lack the Heather Ale.

It fortuned that his vassals,
    Riding free on the heath,
Came on a stone that was fallen
    And vermin hid beneath.
Rudely plucked from their hiding,
    Never a word they spoke:
A son and his aged father—
    Last of the dwarfish folk.

The king sat high on his charger,
    He looked on the little men;
And the dwarfish and swarthy couple
    Looked at the king again.
Down by the shore he had them;
    And there on the giddy brink—
"I will give ye life, ye vermin,
    For the secret of the drink."

There stood the son and father
    And they looked high and low:
The heather was red around them,
    The sea rumbled below.
And up and spoke the father,
    Shrill was his voice to hear:
"I have a word in private,
    A word for the royal ear.

"Life is dear to the aged,
    And honour a little thing;

13

I would gladly sell the secret,"
　Quoth the Pict to the king.
His voice was small as a sparrow's,
　And shrill and wonderful clear;
" I would gladly sell my secret,
　Only my son I fear.

" For life is a little matter
　And death is nought to the young;
And I dare not sell my honour
　Under the eye of my son.
Take him, O king, and bind him,
　And cast him far in the deep;
And it's I will tell the secret
　That I have sworn to keep."

They took the son and bound him,
　Neck and heels in a thong,
And a lad took him and swung him,
　And flung him far and strong,
And the sea swallowed his body,
　Like that of a child of ten;—
And there on the cliff stood the father,
　Last of the dwarfish men.

" True was the word I told you:
　Only my son I feared;
For I doubt the sapling courage
　That goes without the beard.
But now in vain is the torture,
　Fire shall never avail:
Here dies in my bosom
　The secret of Heather Ale."

ROBERT LOUIS STEVENSON

PAUL REVERE'S RIDE

Listen, my children, and you shall hear
Of the midnight ride of Paul Revere,
On the eighteenth of April, in Seventy-five;
Hardly a man is now alive
Who remembers that famous day and year.

He said to his friend, " If the British march
By land or sea from the town to-night,
Hang a lantern aloft in the belfry arch
Of the North Church tower as a signal light,—
One, if by land, and two, if by sea;
And I on the opposite shore will be,
Ready to ride and spread the alarm
Through every Middlesex village and farm,
For the country folk to be up and to arm."

Then he said, " Good night! " and with muffled oar
Silently rowed to the Charlestown shore,
Just as the moon rose over the bay,
Where swinging wide at her moorings lay
The Somerset, British man-of-war;
A phantom ship, with each mast and spar
Across the moon like a prison bar,
And a huge black hulk, that was magnified
By its own reflection in the tide.

Meanwhile, his friend, through alley and street,
Wanders and watches with eager ears,
Till in the silence around him he hears

The muster of men at the barrack door,
The sound of arms, and the tramp of feet,
And the measured tread of the grenadiers,
Marching down to their boats on the shore.

Then he climbed the tower of the Old North Church.
Up the wooden stairs, with stealthy tread,
To the belfry-chamber overhead,
And startled the pigeons from their perch
On the sombre rafters, that round him **made**
Masses and moving shapes of shade,—
By the trembling ladder, steep and tall,
To the highest window in the wall,
Where he paused to listen and look down
A moment on the roofs of the town,
And the moonlight flowing over all.

Beneath, in the churchyard, lay the dead,
In their night-encampment on the hill,
Wrapped in silence so deep and still
That he could hear, like a sentinel's tread,
The watchful night-wind, as it went,
Creeping along from tent to tent,
And seeming to whisper, "All is well!"
A moment only he feels the spell
Of the place and the hour, and the secret dread
Of the lonely belfry and the dead;
For suddenly all his thoughts are bent
On a shadowy something far away,
Where the river widens to meet the bay,—
A line of black that bends and floats
On the rising tide, like a bridge of boats.

Meanwhile, impatient to mount and ride,
Booted and spurred, with a heavy stride
On the opposite shore walked Paul Revere.
Now he patted his horse's side,
Now gazed at the landscape far and near,
Then, impetuous, stamped the earth,
And turned and tightened his saddle-girth;
But mostly he watched with eager search
The belfry-tower of the Old North Church,
As it rose above the graves on the hill,
Lonely and spectral and sombre and still.
And lo! as he looks, on the belfry's height
A glimmer, and then a gleam of light!
He springs to the saddle, the bridle he turns,
But lingers and gazes, till full on his sight
A second lamp in the belfry burns!

A hurry of hoofs in a village street,
A shape in the moonlight, a bulk in the dark,
And beneath, from the pebbles, in passing, a spark
Struck out by a steed flying fearless and fleet;
That was all! And yet, through the gloom and the
    light,
The fate of a nation was riding that night;
And the spark struck out by that steed, in his flight,
Kindled the land into flame with its heat.

He has left the village and mounted the steep,
And beneath him, tranquil and broad and deep,
Is the Mystic, meeting the ocean tides;
And under the alders, that skirt its edge,
Now soft on the sand, now loud on the ledge,
Is heard the tramp of his steed as he rides.

It was twelve by the village clock
When he crossed the bridge into Medford town.
He heard the crowing of the cock,
And the barking of the farmer's dog,
And felt the damp of the river fog,
That rises after the sun goes down.

It was one by the village clock
When he galloped into Lexington.
He saw the gilded weathercock
Swim in the moonlight as he passed,
And the meeting-house windows, blank and bare,
Gaze at him with a spectral glare,
As if they already stood aghast
At the bloody work they would look upon.

It was two by the village clock
When he came to the bridge in Concord town.
He heard the bleating of the flock,
And the twitter of birds among the trees,
And felt the breath of the morning breeze
Blowing over the meadows brown.
And one was safe and asleep in his bed
Who at the bridge would be first to fall,
Who that day would be lying dead,
Pierced by a British musket-ball.

You know the rest. In the books you have read,
How the British Regulars fired and fled,—
How the farmers gave them ball for ball
From behind each fence and farmyard wall
Chasing the red-coats down the lane,
Then crossing the fields to emerge again

Under the trees at the turn of the road,
And only pausing to fire and load.
So through the night rode Paul Revere;
And so through the night went his cry of alarm
To every Middlesex village and farm,—
A cry of defiance, and not of fear,
A voice in the darkness, a knock at the door,
And a word that shall echo evermore!
For, borne on the night-wind of the Past,
Through all our history, to the last,
In the hour of darkness and peril and need,
The people will waken and listen and hear
The hurrying hoof-beats of that steed,
And the midnight message of Paul Revere.

HENRY WADSWORTH LONGFELLOW

OFF THE GROUND

Three jolly Farmers
Once bet a pound
Each dance the others would
Off the ground.
Out of their coats
They slipped right soon,
And neat and nicesome
Put each his shoon.
One—Two—Three!
And away they go,
Not too fast,
And not too slow;
Out from the elm-tree's

Noonday shadow,
Into the sun
And across the meadow.
Past the schoolroom,
With knees well bent,
Fingers a-flicking,
They dancing went.
Upsides and over,
And round and round,
They crossed click-clacking
The Parish bound;
By Tupman's meadow
They did their mile,
Tee-to-tum
On a three-barred stile.
Then straight through Whipham,
Downhill to Week,
Footing it lightsome,
But not too quick,
Up fields to Watchet,
And on through Wye,
Till seven fine churches
They'd seen skip by—
Seven fine churches,
And five old mills,
Farms in the valley,
And sheep on the hills;
Old Man's Acre
And Dead Man's Pool
All left behind,
As they danced through Wool.
And Wool gone by,

Like tops that seem
To spin in sleep
They danced in dream:
Withy—Wellover—
Wassop—Wo—
Like an old clock
Their heels did go.
A league and a league
And a league they went,
And not one weary,
And not one spent,
And lo, and behold!
Past Willow-cum-Leigh
Stretched with its waters
The great green sea.
Says Farmer Bates,
" I puffs and I blows,
What's under the water,
Why, no man knows! "
Says Farmer Giles,
" My mind comes weak,
And a good man drownded
Is far to seek."
But Farmer Turvey,
On twirling toes,
Ups with his gaiters,
And in he goes:
Down where the mermaids
Pluck and play
On their twangling harps
In a sea-green day;
Down where the mermaids,

Finned and fair,
Sleek with their combs
Their yellow hair. . . .
Bates and Giles
On the shingle sat,
Gazing at Turvey's
Floating hat.
But never a ripple
Nor bubble told
Where he was supping
Off plates of gold.
Never an echo
Rilled through the sea
Of the feasting and dancing
And minstrelsy.
They called—called—called:
Came no reply:
Nought but the ripples'
Sandy sigh.
Then glum and silent
They sat instead,
Vacantly brooding
On home and bed,
Till both together
Stood up and said:—
"Us knows not, dreams not,
Where you be,
Turvey, unless
In the deep blue sea;
But axcusing silver—
And it comes most willing—
Here's us two paying

Our forty shilling;
For it's sartin sure, Turvey,
Safe and sound,
You danced us square, Turvey,
Off the ground! "

WALTER DE LA MARE

BARBARA FRIETCHIE

Up from the meadows rich with corn,
Clear in the cool September morn,
The clustered spires of Frederick stand
Green-walled by the hills of Maryland.

Round about them orchards sweep,
Apple and peach tree fruited deep,
Fair as the garden of the Lord
To the eyes of the famished rebel horde,

On that pleasant morn of the early fall
When Lee marched over the mountain-wall,—
Over the mountains winding down,
Horse and foot, into Frederick town.

Forty flags with their silver stars,
Forty flags with their crimson bars,
Flapped in the morning wind: the sun
Of noon looked down, and saw not one.

Up rose old Barbara Frietchie then,
Bowed with her fourscore years and ten;
Bravest of all in Frederick town,
She took up the flag the men hauled down;

23

In her attic window the staff she set,
To show that one heart was loyal yet.
Up the street came the rebel tread,
Stonewall Jackson riding ahead.

Under his slouched hat, left and right,
He glanced; the old flag met his sight.
"Halt!"—the dust-brown ranks stood fast.
"Fire!"—out blazed the rifle blast.

It shivered the window, pane and sash;
It rent the banner with seam and gash.
Quick, as it fell, from the broken staff
Dame Barbara snatched the silken scarf.

She leaned far out on the window sill,
And shook it forth with a royal will.
"Shoot, if you must, this old grey head,
But spare your country's flag," she said.

A shade of sadness, a blush of shame,
Over the face of the leader came;
The noble nature within him stirred
To life, at that woman's deed and word.

"Who touches a hair on yon grey head
Dies like a dog! March on!" he said.
All day long through Frederick Street
Sounded the tread of marching feet;

All day long the free flag toss'd
Over the heads of the rebel host;
Ever its torn folds rose and fell
On the loyal winds, that loved it well.

'And through the hill-gaps sunset light
Shone over it with a warm good-night,
Barbara Frietchie's work is o'er,
And the rebel rides on his raids no more.

J. G. WHITTIER

THE BALLAD OF RICHARD PEAKE

This is the tale of Richard Peake,
   Of Tavistock in Devon,
And the fight he fought in Xeres town—
   God rest his soul in Heaven!

I know each pool of Dart and Exe
   Where trout or grayling hide,
I know the moors from sea to sea
   And where the red-deer bide;
I know a tall ship stem to stern,
   What sail to set or strike,
I know to point a culverin *early form of cannon*
   And how to thrust a pike.
I know the star-way through the night
   And the bodings in the skies,
But many a man knows more than I
   That is not wondrous wise.
I cannot turn a silken phrase,
   Nor make a sonnet sing;
Yet must I write my chronicle
   For my good Lord the King.

25

A western man and lowly born,
  And early sent to sea—
So simple as my breeding was,
  Let this my record be.

Ye have heard my Lord of Essex
  How he sailed to Cadiz Bay,
With all King Charles' men of war
  Upon a Saturday.
We were sixteen sail of Holland,
  And a hundred of the line,
And I was pricked a volunteer
  Aboard the *Convertine*.
We had stormed the fort and castle
  From rising of the sun,
And long ere noon they landed
  And silenced every gun.
But I was no shore soldier,
  And so on board must bide
What time my Lord of Essex
  Marched up the countryside.

Now it fell on the Monday morning
  I took my leave ashore,
And walked up through the orange groves
  A mile might be, or more.
'Twas said the countryside was bare,
  The country-folk in flight,
A score of miles round Cadiz town,
  And not a Don in sight—
When suddenly a cavalier
  His long sword at the thrust

Came spurring down the narrow way
  With a clatter through the dust.
His steed was checked, his grip was loosed,
  With a flap from my blue cloak;
I clutched the rider by the heel,
  And caught the muffled stroke;
I dragged him down upon his face
  And stripped him where he lay,
I took five silver pieces
  And a horse in that affray.
But while he begged his life in words
  That lisp on English ears,
There stole down through the orange groves
  His squad of musketeers:
And when my hands were bound behind,
  That knight to his disgrace
Took back the sword I stripped him of
  And slashed me in the face.
With seven guards on either hand
  And this brave knight before,
They brought me bound and bloody
  In through the city door;
They gored my back with halberds
  And spat into my face.
The urchins called me heathen swine,
  God gave them little grace!
They threw me into prison
  So bloodless and so weak,
It needed all their leeches
  To find me strength to speak;
And vain it was my Captain sent
  To ransom Richard Peake.

I saw our frigates hoisting sail
  Upon the seventh day,
And through my dungeon window
  I watched them fade away.
Two Irish monks came every noon
  And wasted pious breath,
Abjuring me from heresy
  Since I must die the death;
And when a week had passed they said
  It was the Governor's mind
That I should thence to Xeres town
  To the torture they divined.

In Xeres Duke Medina lay
  With many a Count and Earl,
And gravely these good lords were met
  To try the English churl.
It was a pleasant sight to see
  Where they sat in double rows,
Such ruffles and such velvet cloaks
  And slashen sleeves and hose!
The Duke sat at the table's head
  With the King's golden chain—
I mind no finer gentlemen
  Than gentlemen in Spain.
And there and then Medina's self
  Rebuked that craven knight
Who struck the prisoner in the face
  He dared not face in fight.
They plied me well with questions—
  What guns were in the fleet?
What ship was mine? What captain?

And I answered as was meet.
They asked how strong the fort was
  That watches Plymouth Sound,
And boastfully I lied my best
  As a Devon man was bound.
Quoth one, "Why spared ye Cadiz?
  Your fleet put back to sea!"
"Who loots," said I, "in palaces
  May let the almshouse be."
But all this while the soldiers round
  Made mirth each time I spoke,
And ugly words for English ears
  Went round the common folk:
Until some jest rang o'er the rest,
  And all those nobles smiled;
Now God forbid that I should stand
  And hear my land reviled.

I said, "Your king keeps gallant troops
  To wear such bands and cuffs,
And they should hold in battle firm
  When the starch is in their ruffs.
Yet were I free to pick my choice
  From a score of oaken sticks,
I'd stand and play my quarterstaff—
  For life or death with six."
"Now, by the rood," Medina said,
  "A braggart though thou be,
I will not take thee at thy word,
  But fight thou shalt with three!"

And if I made so bold a face
  Be sure it was not pride,

29

But Richard Peake of Tavistock
　　Had heard his land belied.
I deemed my death was long resolved,
　　So basely would not die,
And three to one were heavy odds
　　For a better man than I.
A halberd was my quarterstaff—
　　They knocked the blade away,
The iron spike which shod the butt
　　Stood me in stead that day.
I swung the halberd round my head
　　And felt my might again,
And I took my stand for England
　　Against the arch-foe Spain.

Then out stepped three hidalgos,
　　Steel armoured cap-a-pie,
And lightly sprang into the lists
　　With a mocking bow to me.
God save my Lord—though I must speak—
　　It was a pretty fight.
Three long swords thrust and feinted
　　In front, to left, to right;
While round their heads the halberd swung
　　And as they closed up near,
I snapped two blades—then shortened grip
　　And used it as a spear;
I drove it at the third one's breast,
　　And a horrid wound it made,
The iron butt went through his heart
　　And out by the shoulder-blade.
And now befell a wondrous thing—

30

I needs must say again
Earth holds no finer gentlemen
Than the gentlemen of Spain.

Those nobles rose and clapped their hands,
The Duke was first to speak,
He bade no man on pain of death
Lay hands on Richard Peake.
They gave me gold, a band and cuffs,
This cloak I wear, the ring,
And sent me forth, escorted well
To see the Spanish King;
And in Madrid on Christmas Day
I knelt before his sight,
Resolving all his questionings
With what poor wit I might.
He would have had me bide in Spain
To serve on shore or sea,
But I've a wife by Tavy side
And she's got none but me.
Wherefore he pitied my estate
And pardon free bestowed,
With a hundred pistoles in my scrip
For charges on the road.
And so I bade Madrid farewell,
And came without annoy
Through France to Bordeaux haven,
And thence took ship for Foy.

Now while the Tamar winds to sea,
And while the Tavy runs,
God bless my old west country,
And God bless all her sons!

It's not in vain we've tracked the deer
    By dale and moor and fen,
And drunk the morning with our lips,
    And grown up brawny men.
It's not in vain we swam the Sound,
    And tugged the heavy oar,
And braced the nerve and trained the limbs
    That English mothers bore.
And therefore when the fight goes hard,
    And the many meet the few,
She'll still find hands to do the work
    That English lads must do.
So here I render thanks to God,
    Who brought me through the sea,
Across the desert, back again,
    My mother-land, to thee.
This was the tale of Richard Peake
    Of Tavistock in Devon,
And the fight he fought in Xeres town—
    God rest his soul in Heaven!

LORD RENNELL OF RODD

HERVÉ RIEL

On the sea and at the Hogue, sixteen hundred and
    ninety-two,
  Did the English fight the French,—woe to France!
And, the thirty-first of May, helter-skelter through the
    blue,
Like a crowd of frightened porpoises a shoal of sharks
    pursue,

Came crowding ship on ship to Saint-Malo on the
    Rance,
With the English fleet in view.

'Twas the squadron that escaped, with the victor in full
    chase;
  First and foremost of the drove, in his great ship,
    Damfreville;
    Close on him fled, great and small,
    Twenty-two good ships in all;
And they signalled to the place
" Help the winners of a race!
  Get us guidance, give us harbour, take us quick—or,
    quicker still,
  Here's the English can and will! "

Then the pilots of the place put out brisk and leapt on
    board;
  " Why, what hope or chance have ships like these to
    pass? " laughed they:
" Rocks to starboard, rocks to port, all the passage scarred
    and scored—
Shall the *Formidable* here, with her twelve and eighty
    guns,
  Think to make the river-mouth by a single narrow
    way,
Trust to enter—where 'tis ticklish for a craft of twenty
    tons,
    And with flow at full beside?
    Now, 'tis slackest ebb of tide.
  Reach the mooring? Rather say,
While rock stands or water runs,
  Not a ship will leave the bay! "

Then was called a council straight.
Brief and bitter the debate:
" Here's the English at our heels; would you have them
  take in tow
All that's left us of the fleet, linked together stern and
  bow,
For a prize to Plymouth Sound?
Better run the ships aground! "
 (Ended Damfreville his speech).
" Not a minute more to wait!
 Let the Captains all and each
 Shove ashore, then blow up, burn the vessels on the
  beach!
France must undergo her fate.

" Give the word! " But no such word
Was ever spoke or heard;
 For up stood, for out stepped, for in struck amid all
  these—
A Captain? A Lieutenant? A Mate—first, second,
  third?
  No such man of mark, and meet
  With his betters to compete!
 But a simple Breton sailor pressed by Tourville for the
  fleet,
A poor coasting-pilot he, Hervé Riel the Croisickese.

And, " What mockery or malice have we here? " cries
  Hervé Riel:
 " Are you mad, you Malouins? Are you cowards,
  fools, or rogues?
Talk to me of rocks and shoals, me who took the sound-
  ings, tell

34

On my fingers every bank, every shallow, every swell
    'Twixt the offing here and Grève where the river dis-
        embogues?[1]
Are you bought by English gold? Is it love the lying's
      for?
    Morn and eve, night and day,
    Have I piloted your bay,
Entered free and anchored fast at the foot of Solidor.
    Burn the fleet and ruin France? That were worse than
      fifty Hogues!
      Sirs, they know I speak the truth! Sirs, believe me
      there's a way!

"Only let me lead the line,
    Have the biggest ship to steer,
    Get this *Formidable* clear,
Make the others follow mine,
And I lead them, most and least, by a passage I know
    well,
    Right to Solidor past Grève,
      And there lay them safe and sound;
    And if one ship misbehave,—
      Keel so much as grate the ground—
Why, I've nothing but my life,—here's my head! " cries
    Hervé Riel.

Not a minute more to wait.
" Steer us in, then, small and great!
    Take the helm, lead the line, save the squadron! "
    cried its chief.
Captains, give the sailor place!
    He is Admiral, in brief.

[1] Falls into the sea.

Still the north wind, by God's grace!
See the noble fellow's face,
As the big ship, with a bound,
Clears the entry like a hound,
Keeps the passage, as its inch of way were the wide sea's
     profound!
  See, safe thro' shoal and rock,
  How they follow in a flock,
Not a ship that misbehaves, not a keel that grates the
     ground,
  Not a spar that comes to grief!
The peril, see, is past,
All are harboured to the last,
And just as Hervé Riel hollas " Anchor! "—sure as fate,
Up the English come—too late!

So, the storm subsides to calm :
  They see the green trees wave
  On the heights o'erlooking Grève.
Hearts that bled are staunch'd with balm,
" Just our rapture to enhance,
  Let the English rake the bay,
Gnash their teeth and glare askance
  As they cannonade away!
'Neath rampired Solidor pleasant riding on the Rance! "
Now hope succeeds despair on each Captain's counten-
     ance!
Out burst all with one accord,
   " This is Paradise for Hell!
  Let France, let France's King
  Thank the man that did the thing! "
What a shout, and all one word,

"Hervé Riel!"
As he stepped in front once more,
  Not a symptom of surprise
  In the frank blue Breton eyes,
Just the same man as before.

Then said Damfreville, "My friend,
I must speak out at the end,
  Though I find the speaking hard.
Praise is deeper than the lips:
You have saved the King his ships,
  You must name your own reward.
'Faith our sun was near eclipse!
Demand whate'er you will,
France remains your debtor still.
Ask to heart's content and have! or my name's not
    Damfreville."

Then a beam of fun outbroke
On the bearded mouth that spoke,
As the honest heart laughed through
Those frank eyes of Breton blue:
"Since I needs must say my say,
  Since on board the duty's done,
    And from Malo Roads to Croisic Point, what is it but
    a run?—
Since 'tis ask and have, I may—
  Since the others go ashore—
Come! A good whole holiday!
    Leave to go and see my wife, whom I call the Belle
    Aurore!"
    That he asked, and that he got—nothing more.

Name and deed alike are lost:
Not a pillar nor a post
  In his Croisic keeps alive the feat as it befell;
Not a head in white and black
On a single fishing smack,
In memory of the man but for whom had gone to wrack
  All that France saved from the fight whence England
      bore the bell.
Go to Paris, rank on rank
  Search the heroes flung pell-mell
On the Louvre, face and flank!
  You shall look long enough ere you come to Hervé
      Riel.
So, for better and for worse,
Hervé Riel, accept my verse!
In my verse, Hervé Riel, do thou once more
Save the squadron, honour France, love thy wife, the
      Belle Aurore.

ROBERT BROWNING

SAM'S THREE WISHES;
OR LIFE'S LITTLE WHIRLIGIG

" I'm thinking and thinking," said old Sam Shore,
" 'Twere somebody *knocking* I heard at the door."

From the clock popped the cuckoo and cuckooed out
    eight,
As there in his chair he wondering sate. . . .
" There's no one I knows on would come so late,

A-clicking the latch of an empty house
With nobbut inside 'un but me and a mouse. . . .
Maybe a-waking in sleep I be,
And 'twere out of a dream came that tapping to me."
At length he cautiously rose, and went,
And with thumb upon latch awhile listening bent,
Then slowly drew open the door. And behold!
There stood a Fairy!—all green and gold,
Mantled up warm against dark and cold,
And smiling up into his candle shine.
Lips like wax, and cheeks like wine,
As saucy and winsome a thing to see
As are linden buds on a linden tree.

Stock-still in the doorway stood simple Sam,
A-ducking his head, with "Good-e'en to 'ee, Ma'am."

Dame Fairy she nods, and cries clear and sweet,
"'Tis a *very* good-e'en, sir, when such folks meet.
I know thee, Sam, though thou wist not of me,
And I'm come in late gloaming to speak with thee;
Though my eyes do dazzle at glint of your rush,
All under this pretty green fuchsia bush."

Sam ducked once more, smiling simple and slow.
Like the warbling of birds her words did flow,
And she laughed, very merry, to see how true
Shone the old man's kindness his courtesy through.
And she nodded her head, and the stars on high
Sparkled down on her smallness from out of the sky.
"A friend is a friend, Sam, and wonderful pleasant,
And I'm come for old sake's sake to bring thee a present.

Three wishes, three wishes are thine, Sam Shore,
Just three wishes—and wish no more,
All because, ruby-ripe to see,
The pixy-pears burn in yon hawthorn tree,
And your old milch cow, wheresoever she goes
Never crops over the fairy-knowes.
Ay, Sam, thou art old and thy house is lone,
But there's Potencies round thee, and here is one! "

Poor Sam, he stared: and the stars o'erhead
A shimmering light on the elm-tops shed.
Like rilling of water her voice rang sweet,
And the night-wind sighed at the sound of it.
He frowned—glanced back at the empty grate,
And shook very slowly his grey old pate:
"Three wishes, my dear! Why, I scarcely knows
Which be my crany and which my toes!
But I thank 'ee, Ma'am, kindly, and this I'd say,
That the night of your passing is Michaelmas Day;
And if it were company come on a sudden,
Why, I'd ax for a fat goose to fry in the oven! "

And lo, and forsooth! as the words he was uttering,
A rich puff of air set his candle a-guttering,
And there rose in the kitchen a sizzling and sputtering,
With a crackling of sparks and of flames a great flutter-
ing,
And—of which there could be no two opinions—
A smoking-hot savour of sage and onions.
Beam, wall and flagstones the kitchen was lit,
Every dark corner and cranny of it
With the blaze from the hearthstone. Copper and brass
Winked back the winking of platter and glass.

And a wonderful squeaking of mice went up
At the smell of a Michaelmas supper to sup—
Unctuous odours that wreathed and swirled
Where'er frisked a whisker or mouse-tail twirled,
While out of the chimney up into the night
That ne'er-to-be-snuffed-too-much smoke took flight.
' That's one," says the Fairy, finger on thumb,
' So now, Mister Sam, there's but two to come! "

She leaned her head sidelong; she lifted her chin,
With a twinkling of eye from the radiance within.
Poor Sam stood stounded; he says, says he,
" I *wish* my old Mother was back with me,
For if there was one thing she couldn't refuse
'Twas a sweet thick slice from the breast of a goose."
But his cheek grew stiff and his eyes stared bright,
For there, on her stick, pushing out of the night,
Tap-tapping along, herself and no other,
Came who but the shape of his dear old Mother!
Straight into the kitchen she hastened and went,
Her breath coming quick as if all but spent,
" Why, Sam," says she, " the bird be turning,
For my nose tells I that the skin's a-burning! "
And down at the oven the ghost of her sat
And basted the goose with the boiling fat.

" Oho! " cries the Fairy, sweet and small,
" Another wish gone will leave nothing at all."
And Sam sighs, " Bless 'ee, Ma'am, keep the other,
There's nowt that I want now I have my Mother."
But the Fairy laughs softly, and says, says she,
" There's one wish left, Sam, I promised 'ee three.

Hasten your wits, the hour creeps on,
There's calling afield and I'm soon to be gone.
Soon as haps midnight the cocks will crow
And me to the gathering and feasting must go."

Sam gazed at his Mother—withered and wan,
The rose in her cheek, her bright hair, gone,
And her poor old back bent double with years—
And he scarce could speak for the salt, salt tears.
"Well, well," he says, "I'm unspeakable glad:
But—it bain't quite the same as when I was a lad.
There's joy and there's joy, Ma'am, but to tell 'ee the
    truth
There's none can compare with the joy of one's youth.
And if it were possible, how could I choose
But be back in boy's breeches to eat the goose;
And all the old things—and my Mother the most,
To shine again real as my own gatepost.
What wouldn't I give, too, to see again wag
The dumpity tail of my old dog, Shag!
Your kindness, Ma'am, but all wishing was vain
Unless us can both be young again."
A shrill, faint laughter from nowhere came . . .
Empty the dark in the candle-flame . . .

And there stood our Sam, about four feet high,
Snub nose, shock hair, and round blue eye.
Breeches and braces and coat of him too,
Shirt on his back, and each clodhopping shoe
Had shrunk to a nicety—button and hem—
To fit the small Sammie tucked up into them.

42

There was his Mother, too; smooth, clear cheek,
Lips as smooth as a blackbird's beak,
Pretty arched eyebrows, the daintiest nose—
While the smoke of the baking deliciously rose.

" Come, Sammie," she cries, " your old Mammikin's
joy,
Climb up on your stool, supper's ready, my boy,
Bring in the candle, and shut out the night;
There's goose, baked taties and cabbage to bite.
Why, bless the wee lamb, he's all shiver and shake,
And you'd think from the look of him scarcely awake!
If 'ee glour wi' those eyes, Sam, so dark and round,
The elves will away with 'ee, I'll be bound! "
So Sam and his Mother by wishes three
Were made just as happy as happy can be.
And there—with a bumpity tail to wag—
Sat laughing, with tongue out, their old dog, Shag.
To clatter of platter, bones, giblets and juice,
Between them they ate up the whole of the goose.

But time is a river for ever in flow,
The weeks went by as the weeks must go.
Soon fifty-two to a year did grow.
The long years passed, one after another,
Making older and older our Sam and his Mother;
And, alas and alack, with nine of them gone,
Poor Shag lay asleep again under a stone.
And a sorrowful dread would sometimes creep
Into Sam's dreams, as he lay asleep,
That his Mother was lost, and away he'd fare,
Calling her, calling her, everywhere,

In dark, in rain, by roads unknown,
Under echoing hills, and alone, alone.
What bliss in the morning to wake and see
The sun shining green in the linden tree,
And out of that dream's dark shadowiness
To slip in on his Mother and give her a kiss.
Then go whistling off in the dew to hear
The thrushes all mocking him, sweet and clear.

Still, moon after moon from heaven above
Shone on Mother and son, and made light of love.
Her roses faded, her pretty brown hair
Had sorrowful grey in it everywhere.
And at last she died, and was laid to rest,
Her tired hands crossed on her shrunken breast.
And Sam, now lonely, lived on and on
Till most of his workaday life seemed gone.

Yet spring came again with its green and blue,
And presently summer's wild roses too,
Pinks, Sweet William, and sops-in-wine,
Blackberry, lavender, eglantine.
And when these had blossomed and gone their way,
'Twas apples, and daisies, and Michaelmas Day—
Yes, spider-webs, dew, and haws in the may,
And seraphs singing in Michaelmas Day.

Sam worked all morning and *couldn't* get rest
From a kind of feeling of grief in his breast.
And yet, not grief, but something more
Like the thought that what happens has happened
     before.

He fed the chickens, he fed the sow,
On a three-legged stool sat down to the cow,
With a pail 'twixt his legs in the green in the meadow,
Under the elm trees' lengthening shadow;
And woke at last with a smile and a sigh
To find he had milked his poor Jingo dry.

As dusk set in, even the birds did seem
To be calling and calling from out of a dream.
He chopped up kindling, shut up his shed,
In a bucket of well-water soused his head
To freshen his eyes up a little and make
The drowsy old wits of him wider awake.
As neat as a womanless creature is able
He swept up his hearthstone and laid the table.
And then o'er his platter and mug, if you please,
Sate gloomily gooming at loaf and cheese—
Gooming and gooming as if the mere sight
Of his victuals could satisfy appetite!
And the longer and longer he looked at them
The slimmer slimmed upward his candle flame,
Blue in the air. And when squeaked a mouse
'Twas loud as a trump in the hush of the house,
Then, sudden, a soft little wind puffed by,
'Twixt the thick-thatched roof and the star-sown sky;
And died. And then
That deep, dead, wonderful silence again.

Then—soft as a rattle a-counting her seeds
In the midst of a tangle of withered-up weeds—
Came a faint, faint knocking, a rustle like silk,
And a breath at the keyhole as soft as milk—

Still as the flit of a moth.   And then . . .
That infinitesimal knocking again.

Sam lifted his chin from his fists.   He listened.
His wandering eyes in the candle glistened.
Then slowly, slowly, rolled round by degrees—
And there sat a mouse on the top of his cheese.
He stared at this Midget, and it at him,
Over the edge of his mug's round rim,
And—as if it were Christian—he says, "Did 'ee hear
A faint little tap-tap-tap-tapping, my dear?
You was at supper and me in a maze,
'Tis dark for a caller in these lone days,
There's nowt in the larder.   We're both of us old.
And all of my loved ones sleep under the mould,
And yet—and yet—as I've told 'ee before . . ."

But if Sam's story you'd read to the end,
Turn back to page one, and press onward, dear friend;
Yes, if you would stave the last note of this song,
Turn back to page primus, and warble along!
For all sober records of life (come to write 'em),
Are bound to continue—well—ad infinitum!

WALTER DE LA MARE

THE DIVERTING HISTORY OF JOHN GILPIN

Showing how he went farther than he intended, and
came safe home again

John Gilpin was a citizen
Of credit and renown,
A train-band captain eke was he
Of famous London town.

John Gilpin's spouse said to her dear—
" Though wedded we have been
These twice ten tedious years, yet we
No holiday have seen.

" To-morrow is our wedding-day,
And we will then repair
Unto the Bell at Edmonton,
All in a chaise and pair.

" My sister, and my sister's child,
Myself, and children three,
Will fill the chaise; so you must ride
On horseback after we."

He soon replied—" I do admire
Of womankind but one,
And you are she, my dearest dear,
Therefore it shall be done.

" I am a linen-draper bold,
As all the world doth know,
And my good friend the calender[1]
Will lend his horse to go."

Quoth Mrs. Gilpin—" That's well said;
And, for that wine is dear,
We will be furnished with our own,
Which is both bright and clear."

John Gilpin kissed his loving wife;
O'erjoyed was he to find
That, though on pleasure she was bent,
She had a frugal mind.

[1] Maker of cloth.

The morning came, the chaise was brought,
But yet was not allowed
To drive up to the door, lest all
Should say that she was proud.

So three doors off the chaise was stayed,
Where they did all get in;
Six precious souls, and all agog
To dash through thick and thin!

Smack went the whip, round went the wheels,
Were never folk so glad,
The stones did rattle underneath,
As if Cheapside were mad.

John Gilpin at his horse's side
Seized fast the flowing mane,
And up he got, in haste to ride,
But soon came down again;

For saddle-tree scarce reached had he,
His journey to begin,
When, turning round his head, he saw
Three customers come in.

So down he came; for loss of time,
Although it grieved him sore,
Yet loss of pence, full well he knew,
Would trouble him much more.

'Twas long before the customers
Were suited to their mind,
When Betty screaming came downstairs—
" The wine is left behind! "

" Good lack! " quoth he—"yet bring it me,
My leathern belt likewise,
In which I bear my trusty sword
When I do exercise."

Now mistress Gilpin (careful soul!)
Had two stone bottles found,
To hold the liquor that she loved,
And keep it safe and sound.

Each bottle had a curling ear,
Through which the belt he drew,
And hung a bottle on each side,
To make his balance true.

Then, over all, that he might be
Equipped from top to toe,
His long red cloak, well brushed and neat,
He manfully did throw.

Now see him mounted once again
Upon his nimble steed,
Full slowly pacing o'er the stones
With caution and good heed!

But, finding soon a smoother road
Beneath his well-shod feet,
The snorting beast began to trot,
Which galled him in his seat.

So, "Fair and softly," John he cried,
But John he cried in vain;
That trot became a gallop soon,
In spite of curb and rein.

So stooping down, as needs he must
Who cannot sit upright,
He grasped the mane with both his hands,
And eke with all his might.

His horse, who never in that sort
Had handled been before,
What thing upon his back had got
Did wonder more and more.

Away went Gilpin, neck or nought;
Away went hat and wig!—
He little dreamt, when he set out,
Of running such a rig!

The wind did blow, the cloak did fly
Like streamer long and gay,
Till, loop and button failing both,
At last it flew away.

Then might all people well discern
The bottles he had slung;
A bottle swinging at each side,
As hath been said or sung.

The dogs did bark, the children screamed,
Up flew the windows all;
And ev'ry soul cried out—" Well done! "
As loud as he could bawl.

Away went Gilpin—who but he?
His fame soon spread around—
" He carries weight! " " He rides a race! "
" 'Tis for a thousand pound! "

And still, as fast as he drew near,
'Twas wonderful to view
How in a trice the turnpike-men
Their gates wide open threw.

And now, as he went bowing down
His reeking head full low,
The bottles twain behind his back
Were shattered at a blow.

Down ran the wine into the road,
Most piteous to be seen,
Which made his horse's flanks to smoke
As they had basted been.

But still he seemed to carry weight,
With leathern girdle braced;
For all might see the bottle-necks
Still dangling at his waist.

Thus all through merry Islington
These gambols he did play,
Until he came unto the Wash[1]
Of Edmonton so gay.

And there he threw the wash[2] about
On both sides of the way,
· Just like unto a trundling mop,
Or a wild goose at play.

At Edmonton his loving wife
From the balcóny spied
Her tender husband, wond'ring much
To see how he did ride.

[1] A low-lying stretch of land.
[2] Pools of water lying on the marshy ground.

" Stop, stop, John Gilpin!—Here's the house "—
They all at once did cry;
" The dinner waits, and we are tired."
Said Gilpin—" So am I! "

But yet his horse was not a whit
Inclined to tarry there;
For why?—his owner had a house
Full ten miles off, at Ware.

So like an arrow swift he flew,
Shot by an archer strong;
So did he fly—which brings me to
The middle of my song.

Away went Gilpin, out of breath,
And sore against his will,
Till at his friend the calender's
His horse at last stood still.

The calender, amazed to see
His neighbour in such trim,
Laid down his pipe, flew to the gate,
And thus accosted him:—

" What news? what news? your tidings tell;
Tell me you must and shall—
Say why bare-headed you are come,
Or why you come at all? "

Now Gilpin had a pleasant wit,
And loved a timely joke;
And thus unto the calender
In merry guise he spoke:—

"I came because your horse would come;
And, if I well forebode,
My hat and wig will soon be here—
They are upon the road."

The calender, right glad to find
His friend in merry pin,
Returned him not a single word,
But to the house went in;

Whence straight he came with hat and wig;
A wig that flowed behind,
A hat not much the worse for wear,
Each comely in its kind.

He held them up, and, in his turn,
Thus showed his ready wit—
"My head is twice as big as yours,
They therefore needs must fit.

"But let me scrape the dirt away
That hangs upon your face;
And stop and eat, for well you may
Be in a hungry case."

Said John—"It is my wedding-day,
And all the world would stare,
If wife should dine at Edmonton
And I should dine at Ware!"

So, turning to his horse, he said—
"I am in haste to dine;
'Twas for your pleasure you came here,
You shall go back for mine."

Ah, luckless speech, and bootless boast!
For which he paid full dear;
For, while he spake, a braying ass
Did sing most loud and clear;

Whereat his horse did snort, as he
Had heard a lion roar,
And galloped off with all his might,
As he had done before.

Away went Gilpin, and away
Went Gilpin's hat and wig!
He lost them sooner than at first—
For why?—they were too big!

Now, mistress Gilpin, when she saw
Her husband posting down
Into the country far away,
She pulled out half a crown;

And thus unto the youth she said
That drove them to the Bell—
" This shall be yours when you bring back
My husband safe and well."

The youth did ride, and soon did meet
John coming back amain;
Whom in a trice he tried to stop
By catching at his rein;

But, not performing what he meant,
And gladly would have done,
The frighted steed he frighted more,
And made him faster run.

Away went Gilpin, and away
Went post-boy at his heels!—
The post-boy's horse right glad to miss
The lumb'ring of the wheels.

Six gentlemen upon the road,
Thus seeing Gilpin fly,
With post-boy scamp'ring in the rear,
They raised the hue and cry:

"Stop thief! stop thief!—a highwayman!"
Not one of them was mute;
And all and each that passed that way
Did join in the pursuit.

And now the turnpike gates again
Flew open in short space;
The toll-men thinking, as before,
That Gilpin rode a race.

And so he did—and won it too!—
For he got first to town;
Nor stopped till where he had got up
He did again get down.

Now let us sing—Long live the king,
And Gilpin long live he;
And, when he next doth ride abroad,
May I be there to see!

WILLIAM COWPER

THE WELL OF ST. KEYNE

A well there is in the west country,
    And a clearer one never was seen;
There is not a wife in the west country
    But has heard of the Well of St. Keyne.

An oak and an elm-tree stand beside,
    And behind doth an ash-tree grow,
And a willow from the bank above
    Droops to the water below.

A traveller came to the Well of St. Keyne.
    Joyfully he drew nigh,
For from cock-crow he had been travelling,
    And there was not a cloud in the sky.

He drank of the water so cool and clear,
    For thirsty and hot was he,
And he sat down upon the bank
    Under the willow-tree.

There came a man from the house hard by
    At the Well to fill his pail;
On the Well-side he rested it,
    And he bade the stranger hail.

"Now art thou a bachelor, stranger?" quoth he,
    "For an if thou hast a wife,
The happiest draught thou hast drunk this day
    That ever thou didst in thy life.

" Or has thy good woman, if one thou hast,
　　Ever here in Cornwall been?
For an if she have, I'll venture my life
　　She has drunk of the Well of St. Keyne."

" I have left a good woman who never was here,"
　　The stranger he made reply,
" But that my draught should be the better for that,
　　I pray you answer me why."

" St. Keyne," quoth the Cornish-man, " many a time
　　Drank of this crystal Well,
And before the Angel summoned her,
　　She laid on the water a spell.

" If the husband of this gifted Well
　　Shall drink before his wife,
A happy man thenceforth is he,
　　For he shall be master for life.

" But if the wife should drink of it first—
　　God help the husband then! "
The stranger stooped to the Well of St. Keyne,
　　And drank of the water again.

" You drank of the Well I warrant betimes? "
　　He to the Cornish-man said:
But the Cornish-man smiled as the stranger spake,
　　And sheepishly shook his head.

" I hastened as soon as the wedding was done,
　　And left my wife in the porch;
But i' faith she had been wiser than me,
　　For she took a bottle to church."

ROBERT SOUTHEY

57

MARY AMBREE

When captains courageous, whom death could not
    daunt,
Did march to the siege of the city of Gaunt,
They mustered their soldiers by two and by three,
And the foremost in battle was Mary Ambree.

When the brave Sir John Major was slain in her sight,
Who was her true lover, her joy, and delight,
Because he was slain most treacrouslìe,
Then vowed to revenge him, Mary Ambree.

She clothèd herself from the top to the toe
In buff of the bravest, most seemly to show;
A fair shirt of mail then slippèd on she;
Was not this a brave bonny lass, Mary Ambree?

A helmet of proof she straight did provide,
A strong arming sword she girt by her side,
On her hand a goodly fair gauntlet put she;
Was not this a brave bonny lass, Mary Ambree?

Then took she her sword and her target in hand,
Bidding all such, as would, they might be of her band,
To wait on her person came thousand and three;
Was not this a brave bonny lass, Mary Ambree?

" My soldiers," she saith, " so valiant and bold,
Now follow your captain, whom you do behold;
Still foremost in battle myself will I be."
Was not this a brave bonny lass, Mary Ambree?

Then cried out her soldiers, and loud they did say,
So well thou becomest this gallant array,
Thy heart and thy weapons so well do agree,
No maiden was ever like Mary Ambree."

She cheerèd her soldiers, that foughten for life,
With ancient and standard, with drum and with fife,
With brave clanging trumpets, that sounded so free;
Was not this a brave bonny lass, Mary Ambree?

She led up her soldiers in battle array,
Gainst three times their number by break of the day;
Seven hours in skirmish continuèd she;
Was not this a brave bonny lass, Mary Ambree?

She fillèd the skies with the smoke of her shot,
And her enemies' bodies with bullets so hot;
For one of her own men a score killèd she;
Was not this a brave bonny lass, Mary Ambree?

And when her false gunner, to spoil her intent,
Away all her pellets and powder had sent,
Straight with her keen weapon she slasht him in three;
Was not this a brave bonny lass, Mary Ambree?

Being falsely betrayèd for lucre of hire,
At length she was forced to make a retire;
Then her soldiers into a strong castle drew she;
Was not this a brave bonny lass, Mary Ambree?

Her foes they beset her on every side,
As thinking close siege she could never abide;
To beat down the walls they all did decree :
But stoutly defied them brave Mary Ambree.

Then took she her sword and her target in hand,
And mounting the walls all undaunted did stand,
There daring their captains to match any three;
O what a brave captain was Mary Ambree!

"Now say, English captain, what wouldest thou **give**
To ransom thyself, which else must not live?
Come yield thyself quickly, or slain thou must be."
Then smilèd sweetly brave Mary Ambree.

"Ye captains courageous, of valour so bold,
Whom think you before you now you do behold?"
"A knight, sir, of England, and captain so free,
Who shortly with us a prisoner must be."

"No captain of England; behold in your sight
A woman, my masters, and therefore no knight:
No knight, sirs, of England, nor captain you see,
But a poor simple maiden, called Mary Ambree."

"But art thou a woman, as thou dost declare,
Whose valour hath proved so undaunted in war?
If England doth yield such brave maidens as thee,
Full well may they conquer, fair Mary Ambree."

Then to her own country she back did return,
Still holding the foes of fair England in scorn;
Therefore English captains of every degree
Sing forth the brave valours of Mary Ambree.

ANONYMOUS

A KNIGHT OF THE OCEAN-SEA

Sir Humphrey Gilbert, hard of hand,
   Knight-in-chief of the Ocean-sea,
Gazed from the rocks of his New Found Land
   And thought of his home where his heart would be.

He gazed across the wintry waste
   That weltered and hissed like molten lead,—
"He saileth twice who saileth in haste!
   I'll wait the favour of Spring," he said.

      Ever the more, ever the more,
      He heard the winds and the waves roar!
      Thunder on thunder shook the shore.

The yellow clots of foam went by
   Like shavings that curl from a ship-wright's plane,
Clinging and flying, afar and nigh,
   Shuddering, flying and clinging again.

A thousand bubbles in every one
   Shifted and shimmered with rainbow gleams;
But—had they been planets and stars that spun,
   He had let them drift by his feet like dreams;

Heavy of heart was our Admirall,
   For out of his ships,—and they were but three!—
He had lost the fairest and most tall,
   And—he was a knight of the Ocean-sea.

      Ever the more, ever the more,
      He heard the winds and the waves roar!
      Thunder on thunder shook the shore.

Heavy of heart, heavy of heart,
   For she was a galleon mighty as May,
And the storm that ripped her glory apart
   Had stripped his soul for the winter's way;

And he was aware of a whisper blown
   From foc'sle to poop, from windward to lee,
That the fault was his, and his alone,
   And—he was a Knight of the Ocean-sea.

" Had he done that! Had he done this! "
   And yet his mariners loved him well;
But an idle word is hard to miss,
   And the foam hides more than the deep can tell.

And the deep had buried his best-loved books,
   With many a hard-won chart and plan:
And a king that is conquered must see strange looks
   So bitter a thing is the heart of man!

And—" Whom will you find to pay your debt?
   For a venture like this is a costly thing!
Will they stake yet more, tho' your heart be set
   On the mightier voyage you planned for the spring?

He raised his head like a Viking crowned,—
   " I'll take my old flag to her Majestie,
And she will lend me ten thousand pound
   To make her Queen of the Ocean-sea! "

      Ever the more, ever the more,
      He heard the winds and the waves roar!
      Thunder on thunder shook the shore.

Outside—they heard the great winds blow!
  Outside—the blustering surf they heard,
And the bravest there would ha' flinched to know
  That they must be taken at their own word.

For the great grim waves were as molten lead
  —And he had two ships who sailed with three!—
" And I sail not home till the spring," he said,
  "They are too frail for the Ocean-sea."

But the trumpeter thought of an ale-house bench,
  And the cabin-boy longed for a Devonshire lane,
And the gunner remembered a green-gowned wench,
  And the foc'sle whisper went round again,—

" Sir Humphrey Gilbert is hard of hand,
  But his courage went down with his ship may-be,
And we wait for the Spring in a desert land,
  For—*he is afraid of the Ocean-sea.*"

          Ever the more, ever the more,
          He heard the winds and the waves roar!
          Thunder on thunder shook the shore.

He knew, he knew how the whisper went!
  He knew he must master it last or first!
He knew not how much or how little it meant;
  But his heart was heavy and like to burst.

" Up with your sails, my sea-dogs all!
  The wind has veered! And my ships," quoth he,
" They will serve for a British Admirall
  Who is Knight-in-chief of the Ocean-sea! "

His will was like a North-east wind
  That swept along our helmless crew;
But he would not stay on the *Golden Hind*,
  For that was the stronger ship of the two.

" My little ship's company, lads, hath passed
  Perils and storms a-many with me!
Would ye have me forsake them at the last?
  They'll need a knight of the Ocean-sea! "

     Ever the more, ever the more,
     We heard the winds and the waves roar!
     Thunder on thunder shook the shore.

Beyond Cape Race, the pale sun tipped
  The grim grey waves with silver light
Where, ever in front, his frigate dipped
  Eastward, for England and the night.

And still as the dark began to fall,
  Ever in front of us, running free,
We saw the sails of our Admirall
  Leading us home through the Ocean-sea.

     Ever the more, ever the more,
     We heard the winds and the waves roar!
     But he sailed on, sailed on before.

On Monday at noon of the third fierce day
  A-board our *Golden Hind* he came,
With a trail of blood, marking his way
  On the salt wet decks as he walked half-lame.

For a rusty nail thro' his foot had pierced.
  "Come, master-surgeon, mend it for me;
Though I would it were changed for the nails that
    amerced
  The dying thief upon Calvary."

The surgeon bathed and bound his foot,
  And the master entreated him sore to stay;
But roughly he pulled on his great sea-boot
  With—"The wind is rising and I must away!"

I know not why so little a thing,
  When into his pinnace we helped him down,
Should make our eyelids prick and sting
  As the salt spray were into them blown;

But he called as he went—"Keep watch and steer
  By my lanthorn at night!" Then he waved his hand
With a kinglier watch-word, "We are as near
  To heaven, my lads, by sea as by land!"

          Ever the more, ever the more,
          We heard the gathering tempest roar!
          But he sailed on, sailed on before.

Three hundred leagues on our homeward road,
  We strove to signal him, swooping nigh,
That he would ease his decks of their load
  Of nettings and fights and artillery.

And dark and dark that night 'gan fall,
  And high the muttering breakers swelled,
Till that strange fire which seamen call
  "Castor and Pollux," we beheld,

An evil sign of peril and death,
   Burning pale on the high main-mast;
But calm with the might of Gennesareth
   Our Admirall's voice went ringing past,

Clear thro' the thunders, far and clear,
   Mighty to counsel, clear to command,
Joyfully ringing, "We are as near
   To heaven, my lads, by sea as by land!"

      Ever the more, ever the more,
      We heard the raging hurricane roar!
      But he sailed on, sailed on before.

And over us fled the fleet of the stars,
   And, ever in front of us, far or nigh,
The lanthorn on his cross-tree spars
   Dipped to the Pit or soared to the Sky!

'Twould sweep to the lights of Charles's Wain,
   As the hills of the deep 'ud mount and flee,
Then swoop down vanishing cliffs again
   To the thundering gulfs of the Ocean-sea.

We saw it shine as it swooped from the height,
   With ruining breakers on every hand,
Then—a cry came out of the black mid-night,
   As near to heaven by sea as land!

And the light was out! Like a wind-blown spark,
   All in a moment! And we—and we—
Prayed for his soul as we swept thro' the dark;
   For he was a Knight of the Ocean-sea.

Over our fleets for evermore
The winds 'ull triumph and the waves roar
But he sails on, sails on before!

ALFRED NOYES

EDINBURGH AFTER FLODDEN

News of battle!—news of battle!
  Hark! 'tis ringing down the street:
And the archways and the pavement
  Bear the clang of hurrying feet.
News of battle! Who hath brought it?
  News of triumph? Who should bring
Tidings from our noble army,
  Greetings from our gallant King?
All last night we watched the beacons
  Blazing on the hills afar,
Each one bearing, as it kindled,
  Message of the opened war.
All night long the northern streamers
  Shot across the trembling sky:
Fearful lights that never beckon
  Save when kings or heroes die.

News of battle! Who hath brought it?
  All are thronging to the gate;
" Warder—warder! open quickly!
  Man—is this a time to wait? "
And the heavy gates are opened:
  Then a murmur long and loud,
And a cry of fear and wonder
  Bursts from out the bending crowd.

For they see in battered harness
　　Only one hard-stricken man;
And his weary steed is wounded,
　　And his cheek is pale and wan.
Spearless hangs a bloody banner
　　In his weak and drooping hand—
What! can this be Randolph Murray,
　　Captain of the city band?

Round him crush the people, crying,
　　"Tell us all—oh, tell us true!
Where are they who went to battle,
　　Randolph Murray, sworn to you?
Where are they, our brothers—children?
　　Have they met the English foe?
Why art thou alone, unfollowed?
　　Is it weal, or is it woe?"
Like a corpse the grisly warrior
　　Looks from out his helm of steel;
But no word he speaks in answer,—
　　Only with his arméd heel
Chides his weary steed, and onward
　　Up the city streets they ride;
Fathers, sisters, mothers, children,
　　Shrieking, praying by his side.
"By the God that made thee, Randolph!
　　Tell us what mischance hath come."
Then he lifts his riven banner,
　　And the asker's voice is dumb. . . .

Right bitter was the agony
　　That wrung that soldier proud:

Thrice did he strive to answer,
  And thrice he groaned aloud.
Then he gave the riven banner
  To the old man's shaking hand,
Saying: "That is all I bring ye
  From the bravest of the land!
Ay, ye well may look upon it—
  It was guarded well and long,
By your brothers and your children,
  By the valiant and the strong.
One by one they fell around it,
  As the archers laid them low,
Grimly dying, still unconquered,
  With their faces to the foe.
"Ay! ye well may look upon it—
  There is more than honour there,
Else be sure I had not brought it
  From the field of dark despair.
Never yet was royal banner
  Steeped in such a costly dye;
It hath lain upon a bosom
  Where no other shroud shall lie.
Sirs! I charge you, keep it holy;
  Keep it as a sacred thing,
For the stain ye see upon it
  Was the life-blood of your King!"

Woe, and woe, and lamentation!
  What a piteous cry was there!
Widows, maidens, mothers, children,
  Shrieking, sobbing in despair!
Through the streets the death-word rushes,

Spreading terror, sweeping on—
" Jesu Christ! our King has fallen—
O Great God, King James is gone!
Holy Mother Mary, shield us,
Thou who erst didst lose thy Son!
O the blackest day for Scotland
That she ever knew before!
O our King—the good, the noble,
Shall we see him **never more?**
Woe to us, and woe to Scotland!
O our sons, our sons and men!
Surely some have 'scaped the Southron,
Surely some will come again! "
Till the oak that fell last winter
Shall uprear its shattered stem—
Wives and mothers of Dunedin—
Ye may look in vain for them!

WILLIAM EDMONDSTOUNE AYTOUN

THE OLD NAVY

The captain stood on the carronade[1]: " First lieutenant,"
says he,
" Send all my merry men aft here, for they must list
to me;
I haven't the gift of the gab, my sons—because I'm bred
to the sea;
That ship there is a Frenchman, who means to fight
with we.

[1] Naval gun first cast at Carron, near Edinburgh.

And odds bobs, hammer and tongs, long as I've
been to sea,
I've fought 'gainst every odds—and I've gained
the victory!

"That ship there is a Frenchman, and if we don't
take she,
'Tis a thousand bullets to one, that she will capture we;
I haven't the gift of the gab, my boys; so each man
to his gun;
If she's not mine in half an hour, I'll flog each mother's
son.
For odds bobs, hammer and tongs, long as I've
been to sea,
I've fought 'gainst every odds—and I've gained
the victory! "

We fought for twenty minutes, when the Frenchman
had enough;
"I little thought," said he, "that your men were of such
stuff":
Our captain took the Frenchman's sword, a low bow
made to he;
"I haven't the gift of the gab, monsieur, but polite I
wish to be.
And odds bobs, hammer and tongs, long as I've
been to sea,
I've fought 'gainst every odds—and I've gained
the victory! "

Our captain sent for all of us: "My merry men," said
he,

"I haven't the gift of the gab, my lads, but yet I
  thankful be:
You've done your duty handsomely, each man stood
  to his gun;
If you hadn't, you villains, as sure as day, I'd have
  flogged each mother's son,
   For odds bobs, hammer and tongs, as long as
    I'm at sea,
   I'll fight 'gainst every odds—and I'll gain the
    victory!"

FREDERICK MARRYAT

THE SMUGGLER'S LEAP

The fire-flash shines from Reculver cliff,
And the answering light burns blue in the skiff,
   And there they stand,
   That smuggling band,
Some in the water and some on the sand,
Ready those contraband goods to land;
The night is dark, they are silent and still;
At the head of the party is Smuggler Bill.

"Now lower away! come, lower away!
We must be far ere the dawn of the day.
If Exciseman Gill should get scent of the prey,
And should come, and should catch us here, what would
  he say?
Come, lower away, lads—once on the hill,
We'll laugh, ho! ho! at Exciseman Gill."

The cargo's lowered from the dark skiff's side,
And the tow-line drags the tubs through the tide—

> No trick nor flam,
> But your real Schiedam.
"Now mount, my merry men, mount and ride!"
Three on the crupper and one before,
And the led-horse laden with five tubs more;
> But the rich point-lace,
> In the oil-skin case
Of proof to guard its contents from ill,
The "prime of the swag," is with Smuggler Bill.

Merrily now in a goodly row,
Away and away those smugglers go,
And they laugh at Exciseman Gill, ho! ho!
> When out from the turn
> Of the road to Herne,
Comes Gill, wide awake to the whole concern—
Exciseman Gill, in all his pride,
With his Custom-house officers all at his side.
They were called Custom-house officers then;
There were no such things as "Preventive men."

> *Sauve qui peut!* That lawless crew,
Away, and away, and away they flew!
Some dropping one tub, some dropping two;
Some gallop this way, and some gallop that,
Through Fordwich Level—o'er Sandwich Flat;
Some fly that way, and some fly this,
Like a covey of birds when the sportsmen miss;
> These in their hurry
> Make for Sturry,
With Custom-house officers close in their rear,
Down Rushbourne Lane, and so by Westbere,

      None of them stopping,
      But shooting and popping;
And many a Custom-house bullet goes slap
Through many a three-gallon tub like a tap,
      And the gin spirts out
      And squirts all about,
And many a heart grew sad that day
That so much good liquor was so thrown away.

      Sauve qui peut! That lawless crew,
Away, and away, and away they flew.
Some seek Whitstable—some Grove Ferry,
Spurring and whipping like madmen—very—
For the life! for the life! they ride! they ride!
And the Custom-house officers all divide,
And they gallop on after them far and wide.
All, all, save one—Exciseman Gill:
He sticks to the skirts of Smuggler Bill.

Smuggler Bill is six feet high;
He has curling locks, and a roving eye;
He has a tongue and he has a smile
Trained the female heart to beguile,
And there is not a farmer's wife in the Isle,
      From St. Nicholas quite
      To the Foreland Light,
But that eye, and that tongue, and that smile will
    wheedle her
To have done with the grocer and make *him* her tea-
    dealer;
There is not a farmer there but he still
Buys gin and tobacco from Smuggler Bill.

Smuggler Bill rides gallant and gay
On his dapple-grey mare, away, and away,
And he pats her neck, and he seems to say,
"Follow who will, ride after who may,
   In sooth he had need
   Fodder his steed,
In lieu of Lent-corn, with a quicksilver feed;
Nor oats, nor beans, nor the best of old hay,
Will make him a match for my own dapple-grey.
Ho! ho—Ho! ho! " says Smuggler Bill—
He draws out a flask and he sips his fill,
And he laughs "Ho! ho! " at Exciseman Gill.

Down Chislett Lane, so free and so fleet
Rides Smuggler Bill, and away to Up-street;
   Sarre Bridge is won—
   Bill thinks it fun;
"Ho! ho! the old tub-gauging son of a gun—
His wind will be thick, and his breeks be thin,
Ere a race like this he may hope to win."
   Away, away
   Goes the fleet dapple-grey,
Fresh as the breeze, and free as the wind,
And Exciseman Gill lags far behind.
"I would give my soul," quoth Exciseman Gill,
"For a nag that would catch that Smuggler Bill.
No matter for blood, no matter for bone,
No matter for colour, bay, brown or roan,
   So I had but one! "
   A voice cried "Done! "
"Aye, dun," said Exciseman Gill, as he spied
A Custom-house officer close by his side,

75

On a high-trotting horse with a dun-coloured hide.
" Devil take me," again quoth Exciseman Gill,
" If I had but that horse, I'd have Smuggler Bill."

From his using such shocking expressions it's plain
That Exciseman Gill was rather profane.
   He was, it is true,
   As bad as a Jew,
A sad old scoundrel as ever you knew,
And he rode in his stirrups sixteen stone two.
He'd just uttered the words which I've mentioned to you,
When his horse, coming slap on his knees with him,
  threw
Him head over heels, and away he flew,
And Exciseman Gill was bruised black and blue.
   When he arose
   His hands and his clothes
Were as filthy as could be—he'd pitched on his nose,
And rolled over and over again in the mud,
And his nose and his chin were all covered with blood;
Yet he screamed with passion, " I'd rather grill
Than not come up with that Smuggler Bill."
" Mount! Mount! " quoth the Custom-house officer,
  " get
On the back of my Dun, you'll bother him yet.
Your words are plain, though they're somewhat rough,
' Done and Done ' between gentlemen's always enough.
I'll lend you a lift—there—you're up on him—so,
He's a rum one to look at—a devil to go! "
   Exciseman Gill
   Dashed up the hill,
And marked not, so eager was he in pursuit,

The queer Custom-house officer's queer-looking boot.
Smuggler Bill rides on amain.
He slacks not girth and he draws not rein,
Yet the dapple-grey mare bounds on in vain,
For nearer now—and he hears it plain—
Sounds the tramp of a horse—" 'Tis the Gauger again."
   Smuggler Bill
   Dashes round by the mill
That stands near the road upon Monkton Hill.
   " Now speed—now speed—
   My dapple-grey steed:
Thou ever, my dapple, wert good at need.
O'er Monkton Mead, and through Minster Level,
We'll baffle him yet, be he gauger or devil.
   For Manston Cave, away! away!
Now speed thee, now speed thee, my good dapple-grey;
It shall never be said that Smuggler Bill
Was run down like a hare by Exciseman Gill."

Manston Cave was Bill's abode:
A mile to the north of the Ramsgate road
   (Of late they say
   It's been taken away—
That is, levelled, and filled up with chalk and clay,
By a gentleman there of the name of Day).
Thither he urges his good dapple-grey;
   And the dapple-grey steed,
   Still good at need,
Though her chest it pants, and her flanks they bleed,
Dashes along at the top of her speed;
But nearer and nearer Exciseman Gill
Cries " Yield thee! now yield thee, thou Smuggler Bill! "

Smuggler Bill, he looks behind,
And he sees a dun horse come swift as the wind,
And his nostrils smoke and his eyes they blaze
Like a couple of lamps on a yellow post-chaise.
  Every shoe he has got
  Appears red-hot.
And sparks round his ears snap, crackle, and play,
And his tail cocks up in a very odd way;
Every hair in his mane seems a porcupine's quill,
And there on his back sits Exciseman Gill,
Crying "Yield thee! now yield thee, thou Smuggler
 Bill!"

Smuggler Bill from his holster drew
A large horse-pistol, of which he had two,
  Made by Nock;
  He pulled back the cock
As far as he could to the back of the lock;
The trigger he touched, and the welkin rang
To the sound of the weapon, it made such a bang;
Smuggler Bill ne'er missed his aim;
The shot told true on the dun—but there came
From the hole where it entered—not blood—but flame.
  He changed his plan,
  And fired at the man;
But his second horse-pistol flashed in the pan,
And Exciseman Gill with a hearty good will
Made a grab at the collar of Smuggler Bill.

The dapple-grey mare made a desperate bound
When that queer dun horse on her flank she found,
Alack! and alas! on what dangerous ground!

It's enough to make one's flesh to creep
To stand on that fearful verge, and peep
Down the rugged sides so dreadfully steep,
Where the chalk-hole yawns full sixty feet deep,
O'er which that steed took that desperate leap.
It was so dark then under the trees
No horse in the world could tell chalk from cheese.
Down they went—o'er that terrible fall—
Horses, Exciseman, Smuggler, and all.

> Below were found
> Next day on the ground
By an elderly gentleman walking his round
(I wouldn't have seen such a sight for a pound),
All smashed and dashed, three mangled corses,
Two of them human—the third was a horse's—
That good dapple-grey, and Exciseman Gill
Yet grasping the collar of Smuggler Bill.

But where was the Dun? that terrible Dun?
From that terrible night he was seen by none.
There are some people think, though I am not one,
That part of the story all nonsense and fun,
> But the country-folks there
> One and all declare,
When the "Crowner's 'Quest" came to sit on the pair,
They heard a loud horse-laugh up in the air.
> If in one of the trips
> Of the steam-boat *Eclipse*
You should go down to Margate to look at the ships,
Or to take what the bathing-room people call "dips,"
> You may hear old folks talk
> Of that quarry of chalk;

79

Or go over—it's rather too far for a walk,
But a three-shilling drive will give you a peep
At that fearful chalk-pit, so awfully deep,
Which is called to this moment " The Smuggler's Leap."
Nay more, I am told, on a moonshiny night,
If you're " plucky," and not over subject to fright,
And go and look over that chalk-pit white,
   You may see, if you will,
   The ghost of Old Gill
Grabbing the ghost of Smuggler Bill,
And the ghost of the dapple-grey lying between 'em.
I'm told so—I can't say I know one who's seen 'em.
RICHARD HARRIS BARHAM

SIR NICHOLAS AT MARSTON MOOR

To horse, to horse, Sir Nicholas! the clarion's note is
 high;
To horse, to horse, Sir Nicholas! the huge drum makes
 reply:
Ere this hath Lucas marched with his gallant Cavaliers,
And the bray of Rupert's trumpets grows fainter on our
 ears.
To horse, to horse, Sir Nicholas! White Guy is at the
 door,
And the vulture whets his beak o'er the field of Marston
 Moor.

Up rose the Lady Alice from her brief and broken
 prayer.
And she brought a silken standard down the narrow
 turret stair.

Oh, many were the tears that those radiant eyes had
  shed,
As she worked the bright word " Glory " in the gay and
  glancing thread;
And mournful was the smile that o'er those beauteous
  features ran,
As she said, " It is your lady's gift, unfurl it in the van."

" It shall flutter, noble wench, where the best and boldest
  ride,
Through the steel-clad files of Skippon, and the black
  dragoons of Pride;
The recreant soul of Fairfax will feel a sicklier qualm,
And the rebel lips of Oliver give out a louder psalm,
When they see my lady's gew-gaw flaunt bravely on their
  wing,
And hear her loyal soldiers' shout, ' For God and for
  the King! ' "—

'Tis noon; the ranks are broken along the royal line;
They fly, the braggarts of the Court, the bullies of the
  Rhine:
Stout Langley's cheer is heard no more, and Astley's
  helm is down,
And Rupert sheathes his rapier with a curse and with
  a frown;
And cold Newcastle mutters as he follows in the flight,
" The German boar had better far have supped in York
  to-night."

The Knight is all alone, his steel cap cleft in twain,
His good buff jerkin crimsoned o'er with many a gory
  stain:

But still he waves the standard, and cries amid the rout—
" For Church and King, fair gentlemen, spur on and
    fight it out! "
And now he wards a Roundhead's pike, and now he
    hums a stave,
And here he quotes a stage-play, and there he fells a
    knave.

Good speed to thee, Sir Nicholas! thou hast no thought
    of fear;
Good speed to thee, Sir Nicholas! but fearful odds are
    here.
The traitors ring thee round, and with every blow and
    thrust,
" Down, down," they cry, " with Belial, down with him
    to the dust! "
" I would," quoth grim old Oliver, " that Belial's trusty
    sword
This day were doing battle for the Saints and for the
    Lord! "—

The Lady Alice sits with her maidens in her bower;
The grey-haired warden watches on the castle's highest
    tower.
" What news, what news, old Anthony? "—" The field
    is lost and won;
The ranks of war are melting as the mists beneath the
    sun;
And a wounded man speeds hither,—I am old and can-
    not see,
Or sure I am that sturdy step my master's step should
    be."—

" I bring thee back the standard from as rude and rough
    a fray
As e'er was proof of soldier's thews, or theme for
    minstrel's lay.
Bid Hubert fetch the silver bowl, and liquor *quantum
    suff.*;
I'll make a shift to drain it, ere I part with boot and buff;
Though Guy through many a gaping wound is breath-
    ing out his life,
And I am come to thee a landless man, my fond and
    faithful wife!

" Sweet, we will fill our money-bags and freight a ship
    for France,
And mourn in merry Paris for this poor realm's mis-
    chance;
Or if the worst betide me, why, better axe or rope,
Than life with Lenthal[1] for a king, and Peters[2] for a
    pope!
Alas, alas, my gallant Guy!—out on the crop-eared boor,
That sent me with my standard on foot from Marston
    Moor! "

                WINTHROP MACKWORTH PRAED

THE *REVENGE*

(A BALLAD OF THE FLEET)

At Florés in the Azores Sir Richard Grenville lay,
And a pinnace, like a fluttered bird, came flying from
    far away:

[1] Speaker of the House of Commons.
[2] Hugh Peters was Cromwell's chaplain.

"Spanish ships of war at sea! we have sighted fifty-
  three!"
Then sware Lord Thomas Howard: "'Fore God I am
  no coward;
But I cannot meet them here, for my ships are out of
  gear,
And the half my men are sick. I must fly, but follow
  quick.
We are six ships of the line; can we fight with fifty-
  three?"

Then spake Sir Richard Grenville: "I know you are no
  coward;
You fly them for a moment to fight with them again.
But I've ninety men and more that are lying sick ashore.
I should count myself the coward if I left them, my Lord
  Howard,
To these Inquisition dogs and the devildoms of Spain."

So Lord Howard passed away with five ships of war that
  day,
Till he melted like a cloud in the silent summer heaven;
But Sir Richard bore in hand all his sick men from the
  land
Very carefully and slow,
Men of Bideford in Devon,
And we laid them on the ballast down below;
For we brought them all aboard,
And they blest him in their pain, that they were not
  left to Spain,
To the thumbscrew and the stake, for the glory of the
  Lord.

He had only a hundred seamen to work the ship and to
fight,
And he sailed away from Florés till the Spaniard came
in sight,
With his huge sea-castles heaving upon the weather
bow.
" Shall we fight or shall we fly?
Good Sir Richard, tell us now,
For to fight is but to die!
There'll be little of us left by the time this sun be set."
And Sir Richard said again: " We be all good English
men.
Let us bang those dogs of Seville, the children of the
devil,
For I never turned my back upon Don or devil yet."

Sir Richard spoke and he laughed, and we roared a
hurrah, and so
The little *Revenge* ran on sheer into the heart of the foe,
With her hundred fighters on deck, and her ninety sick
below;
For half their fleet to the right and half to the left were
seen,
And the little *Revenge* ran on through the long sea-lane
between.

Thousands of their soldiers looked down from their
decks and laughed.
Thousands of their seamen made mock at the mad little
craft
Running on and on, till delayed

By their mountain-like *San Philip* that, of fifteen hundred tons,
And up-shadowing high above us with her yawning tiers
of guns,
Took the breath from our sails, and we stayed.

And while now the great *San Philip* hung above us like
a cloud
Whence the thunderbolt will fall
Long and loud,
Four galleons drew away
From the Spanish fleet that day,
And two upon the larboard and two upon the starboard
lay,
And the battle thunder broke from them all.

But anon the great *San Philip*, she bethought herself
and went,
Having that within her womb that had left her ill
content;
And the rest they came aboard us, and they fought us
hand to hand,
For a dozen times they came with their pikes and mus-
queteers,
And a dozen times we shook 'em off as a dog that shakes
his ears
When he leaps from the water to the land.

And the sun went down, and the stars came out far
over the summer sea,
But never a moment ceased the fight of the one and the
fifty-three.

Ship after ship, the whole night long, their high-built
    galleons came,
Ship after ship, the whole night long, with her battle-
    thunder and flame;
Ship after ship, the whole night long, drew back with
    her dead and her shame.
For some were sunk and many were shattered, and so
    could fight us no more—
God of battles, was ever a battle like this in the world
    before?

For he said, " Fight on! fight on! "
Though his vessel was all but a wreck;
And it chanced that, when half of the short summer
    night was gone,
With a grisly wound to be drest he had left the deck,
But a bullet struck him that was dressing it suddenly
    dead,
And himself he was wounded again in the side and the
    head,
And he said, " Fight on! fight on! "

And the night went down and the sun smiled out far
    over the summer sea,
And the Spanish fleet with broken sides lay round us
    all in a ring;
But they dared not touch us again, for they feared that
    we still could sting,
So they watched what the end would be.
And we had not fought them in vain,
But in perilous plight were we,
Seeing forty of our poor hundred were slain,

And half the rest of us maimed for life
In the crash of the cannonades and the desperate strife;
And the sick men down in the hold were most of them
    stark and cold,
And the pikes were all broken or bent, and the powder
    was all of it spent;
And the masts and the rigging were lying over the side;
But Sir Richard cried in his English pride,
" We have fought such a fight for a day and a night,
As may never be fought again!
We have won great glory, my men!
And a day less or more
At sea or ashore,
We die—does it matter when?
Sink me the ship, Master Gunner—sink her, split her
    in twain!
Fall into the hands of God, not into the hands of
    Spain! "

And the gunner said, "Ay, ay," but the seamen made
    reply:
" We have children, we have wives,
And the Lord hath spared our lives.
We will make the Spaniard promise, if we yield, to let
    us go;
We shall live to fight again and to strike another blow."
And the lion there lay dying, and they yielded to the foe.

And the stately Spanish men to their flagship bore him
    then,
Where they laid him by the mast, old Sir Richard
    caught at last,

And they praised him to his face with their courtly
    foreign grace;
But he rose upon their decks, and he cried:
" I have fought for Queen and Faith like a valiant **man**
    and true;
I have only done my duty as a man is bound to do;
With a joyful spirit I Sir Richard Grenville die! "
And he fell upon their decks, and he died.

And they stared at the dead that had been so valiant
    and true,
And had holden the power and glory of Spain so cheap
That he dared her with one little ship and his English
    few;
Was he devil or man? He was devil for aught they
    knew,
But they sank his body with honour down into the
    deep,
And they manned the *Revenge* with a swarthier alien
    crew,
And away she sailed with her loss and longed for her
    own;
When a wind from the lands they had ruined awoke
    from sleep,
And the water began to heave and the weather to moan,
And or ever that evening a great gale blew,
And a wave like the wave that is raised by an earthquake
    grew,
Till it smote on their hulls and their sails and their
    masts and their flags,
And the whole sea plunged and fell on the shot-shattered
    navy of Spain,

And the little *Revenge* herself went down by the island
    crags
To be lost evermore in the main.

LORD TENNYSON

SAINT BRANDAN

Saint Brandan sails the northern main;
The brotherhood of saints are glad.
He greets them once, he sails again.
So late!—such storms!—The Saint is mad!

He heard across the howling seas
Chime convent bells on wintry nights,
He saw on spray-swept Hebrides
Twinkle the monastery lights;

But north, still north, Saint Brandan steer'd;
And now no bells, no convents more!
The hurtling Polar lights are near'd,
The sea without a human shore.

At last—(it was the Christmas night,
Stars shone after a day of storm)—
He sees float past an iceberg white,
And on it—Christ!—a living form!

That furtive mien, that scowling eye,
Of hair that red and tufted fell—
It is—Oh, where shall Brandan fly?—
The traitor Judas, out of hell!

90

Palsied with terror, Brandan sate;
The moon was bright, the iceberg near.
He hears a voice sigh humbly: "Wait!
By high permission I am here.

"One moment wait, thou holy man!
On earth my crime, my death, they knew;
My name is under all men's ban;
Ah, tell them of my respite too!

"Tell them, one blessed Christmas night—
(It was the first after I came,
Breathing self-murder, frenzy, spite,
To rue my guilt in endless flame)—

"I felt, as I in torment lay
'Mid the souls plagued by heavenly power,
An angel touch mine arm, and say:
Go hence, and cool thyself an hour!

"'Ah, whence this mercy, Lord?' I said.
The Leper recollect, said he,
*Who ask'd the passers-by for aid,
In Joppa, and thy charity.*

"Then I remember'd how I went,
In Joppa, through the public street,
One morn, when the sirocco spent
Its storms of dust, with burning heat;

"And in the street a Leper sate,
Shivering with fever, naked, old;
Sand raked his sores from heel to pate,
The hot wind fever'd him five-fold.

" He gazed upon me as I pass'd,
And murmur'd: *Help me, or I die!*—
To the poor wretch my cloak I cast,
Saw him look eased, and hurried by.

" Oh, Brandan, think what grace divine,
What blessing must true goodness shower,
If semblance of it faint, like mine,
Hath such inestimable power!

" Well-fed, well-clothed, well-friended, I
Did that chance act of good, that one!
Then went my way to kill and lie—
Forget my good as soon as done.

" That germ of kindness, in the womb
Of mercy caught, did not expire;
Outlives my guilt, outlives my doom,
And friends me in the pit of fire.

" Once every year, when carols wake,
On earth, the Christmas night's repose,
Arising from the sinners' lake,
I journey to these healing snows.

" I stanch with ice my burning breast,
With silence balm my whirling brain.
O Brandan! to this hour of rest,
That Joppan leper's ease was pain! "—

Tears started to Saint Brandan's eyes;
He bow'd his head; he breathed a prayer.
When he look'd up—tenantless lies
The iceberg in the frosty air!

MATTHEW ARNOLD

THE BATTLE OF STAMFORD BRIDGE

" Haste thee, Harold, haste thee North!
  Norway ships in Humber crowd.
Tall Hardrada, Sigurd's son,
For thy ruin this hath done—
  England for his own hath vowed.

" The earls have fought, the earls are fled.
  From Tyne to Ouse the homesteads flame.
York behind her battered wall
Waits the instant of her fall
  And the shame of England's name.

" Traitor Tosti's banner streams
  With the invading Raven's wing;
Black the land and red the skies
When Northumbria bleeds and cries
  For thy vengeance, England's King! "

Since that frighted summons flew
  Not twelve suns have sprung and set.
Northward marching night and day
Has King Harold kept his way.
  The hour is come; the hosts are met.

Morn through thin September mist
  Flames on moving helm and man.
On either side of Derwent's banks
Are the Northmen's shielded ranks;
  But silent stays the English van.

A rider to Earl Tosti comes:
   "Turn thee, Tosti, to thy kin!
Harold thy brother brings thee sign
All Northumbria shall be thine.
   Make thy peace, ere the fray begin!"

"And if I turn me to my kin,
   And if I stay the Northmen's hand,
What will Harold give to my friend this day?
To Norway's king what price will he pay
   Out of this English land?"

That rider laughed a mighty laugh.
   "Six full feet of English soil!
Or, since he is taller than the most,
Seven feet shall he have to boast;
   This Harold gives for Norway's spoil."

"What rider was he that spoke thee fair?"
   Harold Hardrada to Tosti cried.
"It was Harold of England spoke me fair;
But now of his bane let him beware.
   Set on, set on! we will break his pride."

Sudden arrows flashed and flew,
   Dark lines of English leapt and rushed
With sound of storm that stung like hail,
And steel rang sharp on supple mail
   With thrust that pierced and blow that crushed.

And sullenly back in a fierce amaze
   The Northmen gave to the river side.

The main of their host on the further shore
Could help them nothing, pressed so sore.
  In the ooze they fought, in the wave they died.

On a narrow bridge alone one man
  The English mass and fury stays.
The spears press close, the timber cracks
But high he swings his dreadful axe,
  With every stroke a life he slays;

But pierced at last from the stream below
  He falls: the Northmen break and shout.
Forward they hurl in wild onset;
But as struggling fish in a mighty net
  The English hem them round about.

Now Norway's king grew battle-mad,
  Mad with joy of his strength he smote.
But as he hewed his battle-path,
And heaped the dead men for a swath,
  An arrow clove him through the throat.

Where he slaughtered, red he fell.
  O then was Norway's hope undone,
Doomed men were they that fought in vain,
Hardrada slain, and Tosti slain!
  The field was lost, the field was won.

York this night rings all her bells.
  Harold feasts within her halls.
The Captains lift their wine-cups.—Hark!
What hoofs come thudding through the dark
  And sudden stop? What silence falls?

Spent with riding staggers in
  One who cries: " Fell news I bring.
Duke William has o'erpast the sea.
His host is camped at Pevensey.
  Save us, save England now, O King! "

Woe to Harold! Twice 'tis not
  His to conquer and to save.
Well he knows the lot is cast.
England claims him to the last.
  South he marches to his grave.

LAURENCE BINYON

AGINCOURT

Fair stood the wind for France,
When we our sails advance,
Nor now to prove our chance
  Longer will tarry;
But putting to the main,
At Kaux, the mouth of Seine,
With all his martial train,
  Landed King Harry.

And taking many a fort,
Furnish'd in warlike sort,
Marcheth towards Agincourt
  In happy hour;
Skirmishing day by day
With those that stopp'd his way,
Where the French general lay
  With all his power.

Which in his height of pride,
King Henry to deride,
His ransom to provide
　To the king sending;
Which he neglects the while,
As from a nation vile,
Yet with an angry smile
　Their fall portending.

And turning to his men,
Quoth our brave Henry then,
"Though they to one be ten,
　Be not amazèd:
Yet have we well begun,
Battles so bravely won
Have ever to the sun
　By fame been raisèd.

"And for myself," quoth he,
"This my full rest shall be,
England ne'er mourn for me,
　Nor more esteem me:
Victor I will remain,
Or on this earth lie slain,
Never shall she sustain
　Loss to redeem me.

"Poitiers and Cressy tell,
When most their pride did swell,
Under our swords they fell:
　No less our skill is
Than when our grandsire great,

Claiming the regal seat,
By many a warlike feat
  Lopp'd the French lilies."

The Duke of York so dread,
The eager vaward[1] led;
With the main Henry sped,
  Amongst his henchmen.
Exeter had the rear,
A braver man not there;
Heavens! how hot they were
  On the false Frenchmen!

They now to fight are gone;
Armour on armour shone,
Drum now to drum did groan;
  To hear was wonder;
That with the cries they make
The very earth did shake;
Trumpet to trumpet spake,
  Thunder to thunder.

Well it thine age became,
O noble Erpingham,
Which didst the signal aim
  To our hid forces;
When from a meadow by,
Like a storm suddenly,
The English archery
  Stuck the French horses.

[1] Vanguard.

With Spanish yew so strong,
Arrows a cloth-yard long,
That like to serpents stung,
   Piercing the weather;
None from his fellow starts,
But playing manly parts,
And like true English hearts,
   Stuck close together.

When down their bows they threw,
And forth their bilboes drew,
And on the French they flew;
   Not one was tardy;
Arms were from shoulders sent,
Scalps to the teeth were rent,
Down the French peasants went,
   Our men were hardy.

This while our noble king,
His broad sword brandishing,
Down the French host did ding,[1]
   As to o'erwhelm it;
And many a deep-wound lent,
His arms with blood besprent,
And many a cruel dent
   Bruisèd his helmet.

Gloucester, that duke so good,
Next of the royal blood,
For famous England stood,
   With his brave brother,

[1] Beat down with resounding blows.

99

Clarence, in steel so bright,
Though but a maiden knight,
Yet in that furious fight
  Scarce such another.

Warwick in blood did wade,
Oxford the foe invade,
And cruel slaughter made,
  Still as they ran up;
Suffolk his axe did ply,
Beaumont and Willoughby
Bare them right doughtily,
  Ferrers and Fanhope.

Upon Saint Crispin's day
Fought was this noble fray,
Which fame did not delay
  To England to carry:
O when shall Englishmen
With such acts fill a pen,
Or England breed again
  Such a King Harry!

MICHAEL DRAYTON

FLANNAN ISLE

" Though three men dwell on Flannan Isle
To keep the lamp alight,
As we steer'd under the lee, we caught
No glimmer through the night! "

A passing ship at dawn had brought
The news; and quickly we set sail,
To find out what strange thing might ail
The keepers of the deep-sea light.

The winter day broke blue and bright,
With glancing sun and glancing spray,
As o'er the swell our boat made way,
As gallant as a gull in flight.

But, as we near'd the lonely Isle;
And look'd up at the naked height;
And saw the lighthouse towering white,
With blinded lantern, that all night
Had never shot a spark
Of comfort through the dark,
So ghostly in the cold sunlight
It seem'd, that we were struck the while
With wonder all too deep for words.

And, as into the tiny creek
We stole beneath the hanging crag,
We saw three queer, black, ugly birds—
Too big, by far, in my belief,
For guillemot or shag—
Like seamen sitting bolt-upright
Upon a half-tide reef:
But, as we near'd, they plunged from sight,
Without a sound, or spurt of white.

And still too mazed to speak,
We landed; and made fast the boat;

And climb'd the track in single file,
Each wishing he was safe afloat,
On any sea, however far,
So it be far from Flannan Isle:
And still we seem'd to climb, and climb,
As though we'd lost all count of time,
And so must climb for evermore.
Yet, all too soon, we reached the door—
The black, sun-blister'd lighthouse-door,
That gaped for us ajar.

As, on the threshold, for a spell,
We paused, we seem'd to breathe the smell
Of limewash and of tar,
Familiar as our daily breath,
As though 'twere some strange scent of death:
And so, yet wondering, side by side,
We stood a moment, still tongue-tied:
And each with black foreboding eyed
The door, ere we should fling it wide,
To leave the sunlight for the gloom:
Till, plucking courage up, at last,
Hard on each other's heels we pass'd
Into the living-room.

Yet, as we crowded through the door,
We only saw a table, spread
For dinner, meat and cheese and bread;
But all untouch'd; and no one there:
As though, when they sat down to eat,
Ere they could even taste,
Alarm had come; and they in haste

Had risen and left the bread and meat:
For at the table-head a chair
Lay tumbled on the floor.
We listen'd; but we only heard
The feeble cheeping of a bird
That starved upon its perch:
And, listening still, without a word,
We set about our hopeless search.

We hunted high, we hunted low,
And soon ransack'd the empty house;
Then o'er the Island, to and fro,
We ranged, to listen and to look
In every cranny, cleft or nook
That might have hid a bird or mouse:
But, though we search'd from shore to shore,
We found no sign in any place:
And soon again stood face to face
Before the gaping door:
And stole into the room once more
As frighten'd children steal.

Aye: though we hunted high and low,
And hunted everywhere,
Of the three men's fate we found no trace
Of any kind in any place,
But a door ajar, and an untouch'd meal,
And an overtoppled chair.

And, as we listen'd in the gloom
Of that forsaken living-room—
A chill clutch on our breath—

We thought how ill-chance came to all
Who kept the Flannan Light:
And how the rock had been the death
Of many a likely lad:

How six had come to a sudden end,
And three had gone stark mad:
And one whom we'd all known as friend
Had leapt from the lantern one still night,
And fallen dead by the lighthouse wall:
And long we thought
On the three we sought,
And of what might yet befall.

Like curs a glance has brought to heel,
We listen'd, flinching there:
And look'd, and look'd, on the untouch'd meal
And the overtoppled chair.

We seem'd to stand for an endless while,
Though still no word was said,
Three men alive on Flannan Isle,
Who thought on three men dead.

WILFRID WILSON GIBSON

MISS THOMPSON GOES SHOPPING

Miss Thompson at Home. In her lone cottage on the downs,
With winds and blizzards and great crowns
Of shining cloud, with wheeling plover
And short grass sweet with the small white
clover,

104

Miss Thompson lived, correct and meek,
A lonely spinster, and every week
On market-day she used to go
Into the little town below,
Tucked in the great downs' hollow bowl
Like pebbles gathered in a shoal.

So, having washed her plates and cup
And banked the kitchen-fire up,
Miss Thompson slipped upstairs and dressed,
Put on her black (her second best),
The bonnet trimmed with rusty plush,
Peeped in the glass with simpering blush,
From camphor-smelling cupboard took
Her thicker jacket off the hook
Because the day might turn to cold.
Then, ready, slipped downstairs and rolled
The hearthrug back: then searched about,
Found her basket, ventured out,
Snecked the door and paused to lock it
And plunge the key in some deep pocket.
Then as she tripped demurely down
The steep descent, the little town
Spread wider till its sprawling street
Enclosed her and her footfalls beat
On hard stone pavement; and she felt
Those throbbing ecstasies that melt
Through heart and mind, as, happy, free,
Her small, prim personality
Merged into the seething strife
Of auction-marts and city life.
Serenely down the busy stream

She goes a-Marketing.

She visits the Bootmaker.

Miss Thompson floated in a dream.
Now, hovering bee-like, she would stop
Entranced before some tempting shop,
Getting in people's way and prying
At things she never thought of buying:
Now wafted on without an aim:
Until in course of time she came
To Watson's bootshop. Long she pries
At boots and shoes of every size,
Brown football-boots, with bar and stud,
For boys that scuffle in the mud,
And dancing-pumps with pointed toes
Glassy as jet, and dull black bows;
Slim ladies' shoes with two-inch heel
And sprinkled beads of gold and steel—
"How anyone can wear such things! "
On either side the doorway springs
(As in a tropic jungle loom
Masses of strange thick-petalled bloom
And fruits misshapen) fold on fold
A growth of sandshoes rubber-soled,
Clambering the door-posts, branching, spawn-
    ing,
Their barbarous bunches like an awning
Over the windows and the doors.
But, framed among the other stores,
Something has caught Miss Thompson's eye
(O worldliness! O vanity!),
A pair of slippers—scarlet plush.
Miss Thompson feels a conscious blush
Suffuse her face, as though her thought
Had ventured further than it ought.

But O that colour's rapturous singing
And the answer in her lone heart ringing!
She turns (O Guardian Angels stop her
From doing anything improper!),
She turns; and see, she stoops and bungles
In through the sandshoes' hanging jungles,
Away from light and common sense,
Into the shop dim-lit and dense
With smells of polish and tanned hide.

Soon from a dark recess inside,   Mrs. Watson.
Fat Mrs. Watson comes slip-slop
To mind the business of the shop.
She walks flat-footed with a roll—
A serviceable, homely soul,
With kindly, ugly face like dough,
Hair dull and colourless as tow.
A huge Scotch-pebble fills the space
Between her bosom and her face.
One sees her making beds all day.
Miss Thompson let her say her say
" So chilly for the time of year.
It's ages since we saw you here."
Then, heart a-flutter, speech precise,
Describes the shoes and asks the price.
" Them, Miss? Ah, them is six-and-nine."
Miss Thompson shudders down the spine.
(Dream of impossible romance.)
She eyes them with a wistful glance,   Wrestles with
Torn between good and evil. Yes,   a Temptation;
For half-a-minute and no less
Miss Thompson strives with seven devils,

Then, soaring over earthly levels,
Turns from the shoes with lingering touch—
"Ah, six-and-nine is far too much.
Sorry to trouble you. Good day! "

And is Saved.

A little farther down the way
Stands Miles's fish-shop, whence is shed
So strong a smell of fishes dead
That people of a subtler sense
Hold their breath and hurry thence.
Miss Thompson hovers there and gazes:
Her housewife's knowing eye appraises
Salt and fresh, severely cons
Kippers bright as tarnished bronze;
Great cods disposed upon the sill
Chilly and wet, with gaping gill,
Flat head, glazed eye, and mute, uncouth,
Shapeless, wan, old-woman's mouth.
Next, a row of soles and plaice
With querulous and twisted face,
And red-eyed bloaters, golden-grey;
Smoked haddocks ranked in neat array;
A group of smelts that take the light
Like slips of rainbow, pearly bright;
Silver trout with rosy spots,
And coral shrimps with keen black dots
For eyes, and hard and jointed sheath
And crisp tails curving underneath.
But there upon the sanded floor,
More wonderful in all that store
Than anything on slab or shelf,
Stood Miles, the fishmonger, himself.

She visits the Fishmonger,

Mr. Miles.

Foursquare he stood and filled the place.
His huge hands and his jolly face
Were red. He had a mouth to quaff
Pint after pint; a sounding laugh,
But wheezy at the end, and oft
His eyes bulged outwards and he coughed.
Aproned he stood from chin to toe.
The apron's vertical long flow
Warped grandly outwards to display
His hale, round belly hung midway,
Whose apex was securely bound
With apron-strings wrapped round and round.
Outside, Miss Thompson, small and staid,
Felt, as she always felt, afraid
Of this huge man who laughed so loud,
And drew the notice of the crowd.
Awhile she paused in timid thought,
Then promptly hurried in and bought
"Two kippers, please. Yes, lovely weather."
"Two kippers? Sixpence altogether":
And in her basket laid the pair
Wrapped face to face in newspaper.

Then on she went, as one half blind,   Relapses into
For things were stirring in her mind: Temptation:
Then turned about with fixed intent
And, heading for the bootshop, went
Straight in and bought the scarlet slippers, And Falls.
And popped them in beside the kippers.
So much for that. From there she tacked,   She visits the
Still flushed by this decisive act,   Chemist,
Westward, and came without a stop

To Mr. Wren the chemist's shop,
And stood awhile outside to see
The tall big-bellied bottles three—
Red, blue, and emerald, richly bright
Each with its burning core of light.
The bell chimed as she pushed the door.
Spotless the oilcloth on the floor,
Limpid as water each glass case,
Each thing precisely in its place.
Rows of small drawers, black-lettered each
With curious words of foreign speech,
Rose high above the other ware.
The old strange fragrance filled the air,
A fragrance like a garden pink,
But tinged with vague medicinal stink
Of camphor, soap, new sponges, blent
With chloroform and violet scent.

Mr. Wren.

And Wren the Chemist, tall and spare
Stood gaunt behind his counter there.
Quiet and very wise he seemed,
With skull-like face, bald head that gleamed:
Through spectacles his eyes looked kind.
He wore a pencil tucked behind
His ear. And never he mistakes
The wildest signs the doctor makes
Prescribing drugs. Brown paper, string,
He will not use for any thing,
But all in neat white parcels packs
And sticks them up with sealing-wax.
Miss Thompson bowed and blushed, and then
Undoubting bought of Mr. Wren,

Being free from modern scepticism,
A bottle for her rheumatism:
Also some peppermints to take
In case of wind; an oval cake
Of scented soap; a penny square
Of pungent naphthaline to scare
The moth. And after Wren had wrapped
And sealed the lot, Miss Thompson clapped
Them in beside the fish and shoes:
"Good day," she says, and off she goes.

Beelike Miss Thompson, whither next?
Outside, you pause awhile, perplext,
Your bearings lost. Then all comes back
And round she wheels, hot on the track
Of Giles the Grocer: and from there
To Emilie the Milliner,
There to be tempted by the sight
Of hats and blouses fiercely bright.
(O guard Miss Thompson, Powers that Be,
From Crudeness and Vulgarity.)

Is led away by the Pleasures of the Town,

Such as Groceries and Millinery,

Still on from shop to shop she goes
With sharp bird's eye, inquiring nose,
Prying and peering, entering some,
Oblivious of the thought of home.
The town brimmed up with deep-blue haze,
But still she stayed to flit and gaze,
Her eyes ablur with rapturous sights,
Her small soul full of small delights,
Empty her purse, her basket filled.
The traffic in the town was stilled.
The clock struck six. Men thronged the inns.

And Other Allurements;

But at length is Convinced of Indiscretion,Dear, dear, she should be home long since.

And returns home.Then as she climbed the misty downs,
The lamps were lighted in the town's
Small streets. She saw them star by star
Multiplying from afar:
Till, mapped beneath her, she could trace
Each street, and the wide square market-
    place
Sunk deeper and deeper as she went
Higher up the steep ascent.
And all that soul-uplifting stir
Step by step fell back from her,
The glory gone, the blossoming
Shrivelled, and she, a small, frail thing,
Carrying her laden basket. Till
Darkness and silence of the hill
Received her in their restful care
And stars came dropping through the air.

But loudly, sweetly sang the slippers
In the basket with the kippers;
And loud and sweet the answering thrills
From her lone heart on the hills.

MARTIN ARMSTRONG

MAZEPPA'S RIDE[1]

" Bring forth the horse! "—the horse was brought;
  In truth, he was a noble steed,
  A Tartar of the Ukraine breed,
Who look'd as though the speed of thought
Were in his limbs; but he was wild,
  Wild as the wild deer, and untaught,
With spur and bridle undefiled—
  'Twas but a day he had been caught;
And snorting, with erected mane,
And struggling fiercely, but in vain,
In the full foam of wrath and dread
To me the desert-born was led;
They bound me on, that menial throng;
Upon his back with many a thong;
Then loosed him with a sudden lash—
Away!—away!—and on we dash!
Torrents less rapid and less rash.

Away!—away! My breath was gone,
I saw not where he hurried on:
'Twas scarcely yet the break of day,
And on he foamed—away!—away!
The last of human sounds which rose,
As I was darted from my foes,
Was the wild shout of savage laughter,

---

[1] This is the story told by the old Hetman, Mazeppa, to King
Charles of Sweden after the battle of Pultowa. Mazeppa describes
how when he was seventy years younger he fell in love with Theresa,
the daughter of the Count Palatine. On hearing of this, the Count
in a great rage seized the young page, Mazeppa, and inflicted on him
the cruel punishment described in these verses.

Which on the wind came roaring after
A moment from the rabble rout:
With sudden wrath I wrench'd my head,
  And snapp'd the cord, which to the mane
  Had bound my neck in lieu of rein,
And, writhing half my form about,
Howl'd back my curse; but 'midst the tread,
The thunder of my courser's speed,
Perchance they did not hear nor heed:
It vexes me—for I would fain
Have paid their insult back again.
I paid it well in after days:
There is not of that castle gate,
Its drawbridge and portcullis' weight,
Stone, bar, moat, bridge, or barrier left;
Nor of its fields a blade of grass,
  Save what grows on a ridge of wall,
  Where stood the hearth-stone of the hall;
And many a time ye there might pass,
Nor dream that e'er that fortress was.
I saw its turrets in a blaze,
Their crackling battlements all cleft,
  And the hot lead pour down like rain
From off the scorch'd and blackening roof,
Whose thickness was not vengeance-proof.
  They little thought that day of pain,
When launch'd, as on the lightning's flash,
They bade me to destruction dash,
  That one day I should come again,
With twice five thousand horse, to thank
  The Count for his uncourteous ride.
They play'd me then a bitter prank,

When, with the wild horse for my guide,
They bound me to his foaming flank:
At length I play'd them one as frank—
For time at last sets all things even—
   And if we do but watch the hour,
   There never yet was human power
Which could evade, if unforgiven,
The patient search and vigil long
Of him who treasures up a wrong.

Away, away, my steed and I,
   Upon the pinions of the wind,
   All human dwellings left behind;
We sped like meteors through the sky,
When with its crackling sound the night
Is chequer'd with the northern light:
Town—village—none were on our track,
   But a wild plain of far extent,
And bounded by a forest black;
   And, save the scarce seen battlement
On distant heights of some strong hold,
Against the Tartars built of old,
No trace of man. The year before
A Turkish army had march'd o'er;
And where the Spahi's hoof hath trod,
The verdure flies the bloody sod:
The sky was dull, and dim, and gray,
   And a low breeze crept moaning by—
   I could have answer'd with a sigh—
But fast we fled, away, away,
And I could neither sigh nor pray;
And my cold sweat-drops fell like rain

Upon the courser's bristling mane;
But, snorting still with rage and fear,
He flew upon his far career:
At times I almost thought, indeed,
He must have slacken'd in his speed;
But no—my bound and slender frame
  Was nothing to his angry might,
And merely like a spur became:
Each motion which I made to free
My swoll'n limbs from their agony
  Increased his fury and affright:
I tried my voice,—'twas faint and low,
But yet he swerved as from a blow;
And, starting to each accent, sprang
As from a sudden trumpet's clang:
Meantime my cords were wet with gore,
Which, oozing through my limbs, ran o'er;
And in my tongue the thirst became
A something fierier far than flame.

We near'd the wild wood—'twas so wide,
I saw no bounds on either side;
'Twas studded with old sturdy trees,
That bent not to the roughest breeze
Which howls down from Siberia's waste,
And strips the forest in its haste,—
But these were few and far between,
Set thick with shrubs more young and green,
Luxuriant with their annual leaves,
Ere strown by those autumnal eves
That nip the forest's foliage dead,
Discolour'd with a lifeless red,

Which stands thereon like stiffen'd gore
Upon the slain when battle's o'er,
And some long winter's night hath shed
Its frost o'er every tombless head,
So cold and stark the raven's beak
May peck unpierced each frozen cheek:
'Twas a wild waste of underwood,
And here and there a chestnut stood,
The strong oak, and the hardy pine;
  But far apart—and well it were,
Or else a different lot were mine—
  The boughs gave way, and did not tear
My limbs; and I found strength to bear
My wounds, already scarr'd with cold;
My bonds forbade to loose my hold.
We rustled through the leaves like wind,
Left shrubs, and trees, and wolves behind;
By night I heard them on the track,
Their troop came hard upon our back,
With their long gallop, which can tire
The hound's deep hate, and hunter's fire:
Where'er we flew they follow'd on,
Nor left us with the morning sun;
Behind I saw them, scarce a rood,
At day-break winding through the wood,
And through the night had heard their feet
Their stealing, rustling step repeat.
Oh! how I wish'd for spear or sword,
At least to die amidst the horde,
And perish—if it must be so—
At bay, destroying many a foe!
When first my courser's race begun,

I wish'd the goal already won;
But now I doubted strength and speed.
Vain doubt! his swift and savage breed
Had nerved him like the mountain-roe;
Nor faster falls the blinding snow
Which whelms the peasant near the door
Whose threshold he shall cross no more,
Bewilder'd with the dazzling blast,
Than through the forest-paths he pass'd—
Untired, untamed, and worse than wild;
All furious as a favour'd child
Balk'd of its wish; or fiercer still—
A woman piqued—who has her will.

The wood was pass'd; 'twas more than noon,
But chill the air, although in June;
Or it might be my veins ran cold—
Prolong'd endurance tames the bold;
And I was then not what I seem,
But headlong as a wintry stream,
And wore my feelings out before
I well could count their causes o'er:
And what with fury, fear, and wrath,
The tortures which beset my path,
Cold, hunger, sorrow, shame, distress,
Thus bound in nature's nakedness;
Sprung from a race whose rising blood,
When stirr'd beyond its calmer mood,
And trodden hard upon, is like
The rattle-snake's, in act to strike,
What marvel if this worn-out trunk
Beneath its woes a moment sunk?

The earth gave way, the skies roll'd round,
I seemed to sink upon the ground;
But err'd, for I was fastly bound.
My heart turn'd sick, my brain grew sore,
And throbb'd awhile, then beat no more:
The skies spun like a mighty wheel;
I saw the trees like drunkards reel,
And a slight flash sprang o'er my eyes,
Which saw no farther: he who dies
Can die no more than then I died.
O'ertortured by that ghastly ride,
I felt the blackness come and go,
    And strove to wake; but could not make
My senses climb up from below:
I felt as on a plank at sea,
When all the waves that dash o'er thee,
At the same time upheave and whelm,
And hurl thee towards a desert realm.
My undulating life was as
The fancied lights that flitting pass
Our shut eyes in deep midnight, when
Fever begins upon the brain;
But soon it pass'd, with little pain,
    But a confusion worse than such:
    I own that I should deem it much,
Dying, to feel the same again;
And yet I do suppose we must
Feel far more ere we turn to dust:
No matter; I have bared my brow
Full in Death's face—before—and now.

My thoughts came back; where was I? Cold,

And numb, and giddy: pulse by pulse
Life reassumed its lingering hold,
And throb by throb,—till grown a pang
   Which for a moment would convulse,
   My blood reflow'd, though thick and chill;
My ear with uncouth noises rang,
   My heart began once more to thrill;
My sight return'd, though dim; alas!
And thicken'd, as it were, with glass.
Methought the dash of waves was nigh;
There was a gleam too of the sky,
Studded with stars;—it is no dream;
The wild horse swims the wilder stream.
The bright broad river's gushing tide
Sweeps, winding onward, far and wide,
And we are half-way, struggling o'er
To yon unknown and silent shore.
The waters broke my hollow trance,
And with a temporary strength
   My stiffen'd limbs were rebaptized.
My courser's broad breast proudly braves,
And dashes off the ascending waves,
And onward we advance!
We reach the slippery shore at length,
   A haven I but little prized,
For all behind was dark and drear,
And all before was night and fear.
How many hours of night or day
In those suspended pangs I lay,
I could not tell; I scarcely knew
If this were human breath I drew.

With glossy skin, and dripping mane,
　And reeling limbs, and reeking flank,
The wild steed's sinewy nerves still strain
　Up the repelling bank.
We gain the top: a boundless plain
Spreads through the shadow of the night,
　And onward, onward, onward, seems,
　Like precipices in our dreams,
To stretch beyond the sight;
And here and there a speck of white,
　Or scatter'd spot of dusky green,
In masses broke into the light,
As rose the moon upon my right:
　But nought distinctly seen
In the dim waste would indicate
The omen of a cottage gate;
No twinkling taper from afar
Stood like a hospitable star;
Not even an ignis-fatuus rose
To make him merry with my woes:
　That very cheat had cheer'd me then!
Although detected, welcome still,
Reminding me, through every ill,
　Of the abodes of men.

Onward we went—but slack and slow:
　His savage force at length o'erspent,
The drooping courser, faint and low,
　All feebly foaming went.
A sickly infant had had power
To guide him forward in that hour:
　But useless all to me:

His new-born tameness nought avail'd—
My limbs were bound; my force had fail'd,
　　Perchance, had they been free.
With feeble effort still I tried
To rend the bonds so starkly tied,
　　But still it was in vain;
My limbs were only wrung the more,
And soon the idle strife gave o'er,
　　Which but prolong'd their pain:
The dizzy race seem'd almost done,
Although no goal was nearly won:
Some streaks announced the coming sun—
　　How slow, alas! he came!
Methought that mist of dawning gray
Would never dapple into day;
How heavily it roll'd away—
　　Before the eastern flame
Rose crimson, and deposed the stars,
And call'd the radiance from their cars,
And fill'd the earth, from his deep throne,
With lonely lustre, all his own.

Up rose the sun; the mists were curl'd
Back from the solitary world
Which lay around, behind, before.
What booted it to traverse o'er
Plain, forest, river?　Man nor brute,
Nor dint of hoof, nor print of foot,
Lay in the wild luxuriant soil;
No sign of travel, none of toil;
The very air was mute;
And not an insect's shrill small horn,

Nor matin bird's new voice was borne
From herb nor thicket. Many a werst,
Panting as if his heart would burst,
The weary brute stagger'd on;
And still we were—or seem'd—alone.
At length, while reeling on our way,
Methought I heard a courser neigh,
From out yon tuft of blackening firs.
Is it the wind those branches stirs?
No, no! from out the forest prance
  A trampling troop; I see them come!
In one vast squadron they advance!
  I strove to cry—my lips were dumb.
The steeds rush on in plunging pride;
But where are they the reins to guide?
A thousand horse, and none to ride!
With flowing tail, and flying mane,
Wide nostrils never stretch'd by pain,
Mouths bloodless to the bit or rein,
And feet that iron never shod,
And flanks unscarr'd by spur or rod,
A thousand horse, the wild, the free,
Like waves that follow o'er the sea,
  Came thickly thundering on,
As if our faint approach to meet;
The sight re-nerved my courser's feet,
A moment staggering, feebly fleet,
A moment, with a faint low neigh,
  He answer'd, and then fell;
With gasps and glazing eyes he lay,
  And reeking limbs immoveable,
  His first and last career is done!

On came the troop—they saw him stoop,
  They saw me strangely bound along
  His back with many a bloody thong:
They stop, they start, they snuff the air,
Gallop a moment here and there,
Approach, retire, wheel round and round,
Then plunging back with sudden bound,
Headed by one black mighty steed,
Who seem'd the patriarch of his breed,
  Without a single speck or hair
Of white upon his shaggy hide;
They snort, they foam, neigh, swerve aside,
And backward to the forest fly,
By instinct, from a human eye.
  They left me there to my despair,
Link'd to the dead and stiffening wretch,
Whose lifeless limbs beneath me stretch,
Relieved from that unwonted weight,
From whence I could not extricate
Nor him, nor me—and there we lay,
  The dying on the dead!
I little deem'd another day
  Would see my houseless, helpless head.

And there from morn till twilight bound,
I felt the heavy hours toil round,
With just enough of life to see
My last of suns go down on me,
In hopeless certainty of mind,
That makes us feel at length resign'd
To that which our foreboding years
Present the worst and last of fears:

Inevitable—even a boon,
Nor more unkind for coming soon,
Yet shunn'd and dreaded with such care,
As if it only were a snare
    That prudence might escape:
At times both wish'd for and implored,
At times sought with self-pointed sword,
Yet still a dark and hideous close
To even intolerable woes,
    And welcome in no shape.
And, strange to say, the sons of pleasure,
    They who have revell'd beyond measure
In beauty, wassail, wine, and treasure,
Die calm, or calmer, oft than he
Whose heritage was misery:
For he who hath in turn run through
All that was beautiful and new,
    Hath nought to hope, and nought to leave;
And, save the future, (which is view'd
Not quite as men are base or good,
    But as their nerves may be endued,)
    With nought perhaps to grieve:
The wretch still hopes his woes must end,
And Death, whom he should deem his friend,
Appears, to his distemper'd eyes,
Arrived to rob him of his prize,
The tree of his new Paradise.
To-morrow would have given him all,
Repaid his pangs, repair'd his fall;
To-morrow would have been the first
Of days no more deplored or curst,
But bright, and long, and beckoning years,

Seen dazzling through the mist of tears,
Guerdon of many a painful hour;
To-morrow would have given him power
To rule, to shine, to smite, to save—
And must it dawn upon his grave?

The sun was sinking—still I lay
  Chain'd to the chill and stiffening steed;
I thought to mingle there our clay,
  And my dim eyes of death had need;
  No hope arose of being freed:
I cast my last looks up the sky,
  And there between me and the sun
I saw the expecting raven fly,
Who scarce would wait till both should die,
  Ere his repast begun;
He flew, and perch'd, then flew once more,
And each time nearer than before;
I saw his wing through twilight flit,
And once so near me he alit
  I could have smote, but lack'd the strength;
But the slight motion of my hand,
And feeble scratching of the sand,
The exerted throat's faint struggling noise,
Which scarcely could be called a voice,
  Together scared him off at length.
I know no more—my latest dream
  Is something of a lovely star
  Which fix'd my dull eyes from afar,
And went and came with wandering beam,
And of the cold, dull, swimming, dense
Sensation of recurring sense,

And then subsiding back to death,
And then again a little breath,
A little thrill, a short suspense,
  An icy sickness curdling o'er
My heart, and sparks that cross'd my brain—
A gasp, a throb, a start of pain,
  A sigh, and nothing more.

  I woke—Where was I?—Do I see
A human face look down on me?
And doth a roof above me close?
Do these limbs on a couch repose?
Is this a chamber where I lie?
And is it mortal, yon bright eye,
That watches me with gentle glance?
  I closed my own again once more,
As doubtful that my former trance
  Could not as yet be o'er.
A slender girl, long-hair'd, and tall,
Sate watching by the cottage wall;
The sparkle of her eye I caught,
Even with my first return of thought;
For ever and anon she threw
  A prying, pitying glance on me
  With her black eyes so wild and free:
I gazed, and gazed, until I knew
  No vision it could be,—
But that I lived, and was released
From adding to the vulture's feast:
And when the Cossack maid beheld
My heavy eyes at length unseal'd,
She smiled—and I essay'd to speak,

But fail'd—and she approach'd, and made
  With lip and finger signs that said,
I must not strive as yet to break
The silence, till my strength should be
Enough to leave my accents free;
And then her hand on mine she laid,
And smooth'd the pillow for my head,
And stole along on tiptoe tread,
  And gently oped the door, and spake
In whispers—ne'er was voice so sweet!
Even music follow'd her light feet:
  But those she call'd were not awake,
And she went forth; but, ere she pass'd,
Another look on me she cast,
  Another sign she made, to say,
That I had nought to fear, that all
Were near, at my command or call,
  And she would not delay
Her due return:—while she was gone,
Methought I felt too much alone.

She came with mother and with sire—
What need of more?—I will not tire
With long recital of the rest,
Since I became the Cossack's guest.
They found me senseless on the plain,
  They bore me to the nearest hut,
They brought me into life again—
Me—one day o'er their realm to reign!
  Thus the vain fool who strove to glut
His rage, refining on my pain,
  Sent me forth to the wilderness,

Bound, naked, bleeding, and alone,
To pass the desert to a throne,—
　What mortal his own doom may guess?

LORD BYRON

HYND HORN

Hynd Horn's bound, love, and Hynd Horn's free,
　With a hey lillelu, and a how lo lan;
Where was ye born, or in what countrie?
　And the birk and the broom blows bonnie.

In good greenwood, there I was born,
And all my forbears me beforn.

"O seven long years I served the King,
And as for wages I never gat nane;

"But ae sight o' his ae daughter.
And that was through an auger-bore."

Seven long years he served the King,
And it's a' for the sake of his daughter Jean.

The King an angry man was he;
He sent young Hynd Horn to the sea.

He's gi'en his luve a silver wand
Wi' seven silver laverocks sittin' thereon.

She's gi'en to him a gay gold ring
Wi' seven bright diamonds set therein.

"As lang's these diamonds keep their hue,
Ye'll know I am a lover true:

"But when the ring turns pale and wan,
Ye may ken that I love anither man."

He hoist up sails and awa' sail'd he
Till that he came to a foreign countrie.

One day as he look'd his ring upon,
He saw the diamonds pale and wan.

He's left the seas and he's come to the land,
And the first that he met was an auld beggar man.

"What news, what news? thou auld beggar man,
For it's seven years sin I've seen land."

"No news," said the beggar, "no news at a',
But there is a wedding in the King's ha'.

"But there is a wedding in the King's ha',
That has halden these forty days and twa."

"Cast off, cast off thy auld beggar weed,
And I'll gi'e thee my gude grey steed:

"And lend to me your wig o' hair
To cover mine, because it is fair."

"My begging weed is na for thee,
Your riding steed is na for me."

But part by right and part by wrang
Hynd Horn has changed wi' the beggar man.

The auld beggar man was bound for to ride,
But young Hynd Horn was bound for the bride.

When he came to the King's gate,
He sought a drink for Hynd Horn's sake.

The bride came trippin' down the stair,
Wi' the scales o' red gowd in her hair;

Wi' a cup o' the red wine in her hand,
And that she gae to the auld beggar man.

Out o' the cup he drank the wine,
And into the cup he dropt the ring.

" O got ye this by sea or land?
Or got ye it of a dead man's hand? "

" I got it na by sea nor land,
But I got it, madam, of your own hand."

" O I'll cast off my gowns o' brown,
And beg with you frae town to town.

" O I'll cast off my gowns o' red,
And I'll beg wi' you to win my bread.

" O I'll take the scales o' gowd frae my hair,
And I'll follow you for evermair."

She has cast awa' the brown and the red,
And she's follow'd him to beg her bread.

She has ta'en the scales o' gowd frae her hair
And she's follow'd him for evermair.

But atween the kitchen and the ha'
He has let his cloutie cloak down fa'.

And the red gowd shinèd over him a',
  With a hey lillelu, and a how lo lan;
And the bride frae the bridegroom was stown awa'
  And the birk and the broom blows bonnie.

INCIDENT OF THE FRENCH CAMP

You know, we French stormed Ratisbon:[1]
    A mile or so away
On a little mound, Napoleon
    Stood on our storming day;
With neck out-thrust, you fancy how,
    Legs wide, arms locked behind,
As if to balance the prone brow
    Oppressive with its mind.

Just as perhaps he mused " My plans
    That soar, to earth may fall,
Let once my army-leader Lannes
    Waver at yonder wall,"—
Out 'twixt the battery-smokes there flew
    A rider, bound on bound
Full-galloping, nor bridle drew
    Until he reached the mound.

Then off there flung in smiling joy,
    And held himself erect
By just his horse's mane, a boy:
    You hardly could suspect—
(So tight he kept his lips compressed,
    Scarce any blood came through)
You looked twice ere you saw his breast
    Was all but shot in two.

[1] Regensburg, captured by Napoleon in 1809.

" Well," cried he, " Emperor, by God's grace
    We've got you Ratisbon!
The Marshal's in the market-place,
    And you'll be there anon
To see your flag-bird[1] flap his vans
    Where I, to heart's desire,
Perched him! " The Chief's eye flashed; his plans
    Soared up again like fire.

The Chief's eye flashed; but presently
    Softened itself, as sheathes
A film the mother-eagle's eye
    When her bruised eaglet breathes:
" You're wounded! " "Nay," his soldier's pride
    Touched to the quick, he said:
" I'm killed, Sire! " And his Chief beside,
    Smiling the boy fell dead.

                        ROBERT BROWNING

[1] The banner bearing the figure of an eagle.

JOHN WINTER

What ails John Winter, that so oft
   Silent he sits apart?
The neighbours cast their looks on him;
   But deep he hides his heart.

In Deptford streets the houses small
   Huddle forlorn together.
Whether the wind blow or be still,
   'Tis soiled and sorry weather.

But over these dim roofs arise
   Tall masts of ocean ships.
Whenever John Winter looked on them,
   The salt blew on his lips.

He cannot pace the street about,
   But they stand before his eyes!
The more he shuns them, the more proud
   And beautiful they rise.

He turns his head, but in his ear
   The steady Trade-winds run,
And in his eye the endless waves
   Ride on into the sun.

His little child at evening said,
   "Now tell us, Dad, a tale
Of naked men that shoot with bows,
   Tell of the spouting whale!"

He told old tales, his eyes were bright,
   His wife looked up to see,
And smiled on him: but in the midst
   He ended suddenly.

He bade them each good night, and kissed
  And held them to his breast.
They wondered and were still, to feel
  Their lips so fondly pressed.

He sat absorbed in silent gloom.
  His wife lifted her head
From sewing, and stole up to him,
  "What ails you, John?" she said.

He spoke no word. A silent tear
  Fell softly down her cheek.
She knelt beside him, and his hand
  Was on her forehead meek.

But even as his tender touch
  Her dumb distress consoled,
The mighty waves danced in his eyes
  And through the silence rolled.

There fell a soft November night,
  Restless with gusts that shook
The chimneys, and beat wildly down
  The flames in the chimney nook.

John Winter lay beside his wife,
  'Twas past the mid of night.
Softly he rose, and in dead hush
  Stood stealthily upright.

Softly he came where slept his boys,
  And kissed them in their bed;
One stretched his arms out in his sleep:
  At that he turned his head.

And now he bent above his wife,
  She slept a sleep serene,
Her patient soul was in the peace
  Of breathing slumber seen.

At last, he kissed one aching kiss,
  Then shrank again in dread,
And from his own home guiltily
  And like a thief he fled.

But now with darkness and the wind
  He breathes a breath more free,
And walks with calmer steps, like one
  Who goes with destiny.

And see, before him the great masts
  Tower with all their spars
Black on the dimness, soaring bold
  Among the mazy stars.

In stormy rushings through the air
  Wild scents the darkness filled,
And with a fierce forgetfulness
  His drinking nostril thrilled.

He hasted with quick feet, he hugged
  The wildness to his breast,
As one who goes the only way
  To set his heart at rest.

When morning glimmered, a great ship
  Dropt gliding down the shore.
John Winter coiled the anchor ropes
  Among his mates once more.

LAURENCE BINYON

THOMAS RYMER

True Thomas lay o'er yond grassy bank,
  And he beheld a ladie gay,
A ladie that was brisk and bold,
  Come riding o'er the fernie brae.

Her skirt was of the grass-green silk,
  Her mantel of the velvet fine,
At ilka tett[1] of her horse's mane
  Hung fifty silver bells and nine.

True Thomas he took off his hat,
  And bowed him low down till his knee:
"All hail, thou mighty Queen of Heaven!
  For your peer on earth I never did see."

"O no, O no, True Thomas," she says,
  "That name does not belong to me;
I am but the queen of fair Elfland,
  And I'm come here for to visit thee.

"But ye maun go wi' me now, Thomas,
  True Thomas, ye maun go wi' me,
For ye maun serve me seven years,
  Thro' weel or wae, as may chance to be.

"Then harp and carp,[2] Thomas," she said,
  "Then harp and carp alang wi' me;
But it will be seven years and a day
  Till ye win back to yere ain countrie."

[1] A lock of hair.   [2] Converse.

She turned about her milk-white steed,
    And took True Thomas up behind,
And aye whene'er her bridle rang,
    The steed flew swifter than the wind.

For forty days and forty nights
    He wade thro' red blude to the knee,
And he saw neither sun nor moon,
    But heard the roaring of the sea.

O they rade on, and farther on,
    Until they came to a garden green:
"Light down, light down, ye ladie free,
    Some of that fruit let me pull to thee."

"O no, O no, True Thomas," she says,
    "That fruit maun not be touched by thee,
For a' the plagues that are in hell
    Light on the fruit of this countrie.

"But I have a loaf here in my lap,
    Likewise a bottle of claret wine,
And now ere we go farther on,
    We'll rest a while, and ye may dine."

When he had eaten and drunk his fill:—
    "Lay down your head upon my knee,"
The lady sayd, " ere we climb yon hill
    And I will show you fairlies[1] three.

"O see not ye yon narrow road,
    So thick beset wi' thorns and briers?
That is the path of righteousness,
    Tho' after it but few inquires.

[1] Marvels.

" And see not ye that braid, braid road,
  That lies across yon lillie leven?[1]
That is the path of wickedness,
  Tho' some call it the road to heaven.

" And see not ye that bonny road,
  Which winds about the fernie brae?
That is the road to fair Elfland,
  Where you and I this night maun gae.

" But Thomas, ye maun hold your tongue,
  Whatever you may hear or see,
For gin ae word you should chance to speak,
  You will ne'er get back to your ain
    countrie."

He has gotten a coat of the even cloth,
  And a pair of shoes of velvet green,
And till seven years were past and gone
  True Thomas on earth was never seen.

ANONYMOUS

THE YARN OF THE *NANCY BELL*

'Twas on the shores that round our coast
  From Deal to Ramsgate span,
That I found alone on a piece of stone
  An elderly naval man.

His hair was weedy, his beard was long,
  And weedy and long was he.
And I heard this wight on the shore recite,
  In a singular minor key:

[1] ?Lily-covered plain. *Leven* does not appear to be connected
with *lawn.*

" Oh, I am a cook and a captain bold,
   And the mate of the *Nancy* brig,
And a bo'sun tight, and a midshipmite,
   And the crew of the captain's gig."

And he shook his fists and he tore his hair,
   Till I really felt afraid,
For I couldn't help thinking the man had been
      drinking,
   And so I simply said:

" Oh, elderly man, it's little I know,
   Of the duties of men of the sea,
And I'll eat my hand if I understand
   How you can possibly be

" At once a cook, and a captain bold,
   And the mate of the *Nancy* brig,
And a bo'sun tight and a midshipmite,
   And the crew of the captain's gig."

Then he gave a hitch to his trousers, which
   Is a trick all seamen larn,
And having got rid of a thumping quid,
   He spun this painful yarn:

" 'Twas in the good ship *Nancy Bell*
   That we sailed to the Indian sea,
And there on a reef we come to grief,
   Which has often occurred to me.

" And pretty nigh all o' the crew was drowned
   (There was seventy-seven o' soul)
And only ten of the *Nancy's* men
   Said ' Here! ' to the muster roll.

" There was me and the cook and the captain
  bold,
  And the mate of the *Nancy* brig,
And the bo'sun tight and a midshipmite,
  And the crew of the captain's gig.

" For a month we'd neither wittles nor drink,
  Till a-hungry we did feel,
So, we drawed a lot, and accordin' shot
  The captain for our meal.

" The next lot fell to the *Nancy's* mate,
  And a delicate dish he made;
Then our appetite with the midshipmite
  We seven survivors stayed.

" And then we murdered the bo'sun tight,
  And he much resembled pig;
Then we wittled free, did the cook and me,
  On the crew of the captain's gig.

" Then only the cook and me was left,
  And the delicate question, ' Which
Of us two goes to the kettle? ' arose,
  And we argued it out as sich.

" For I loved that cook as a brother, I did,
  And the cook he worshipped me;
But we'd both be blowed if we'd either be stowed
  In the other chap's hold, you see.

" ' I'll be eat if you dines off me,' says TOM,
  ' Yes, that,' says I, ' you'll be,'—
' I'm boiled if I die, my friend,' quoth I,
  And ' Exactly so,' quoth he.

"Says he, 'Dear JAMES, to murder me
   Were a foolish thing to do,
For don't you see that you can't cook *me*,
   While I can—and will—cook *you!*'

"So, he boils the water, and takes the salt
   And the pepper in portions true
(Which he never forgot) and some chopped
     shalot
   And some sage and parsley too.

"'Come here,' says he, with a proper pride,
   Which his smiling features tell,
''Twill soothing be if I let you see,
   How extremely nice you'll smell.'

"And he stirred it round and round and
     round,
   And he sniffed at the foaming broth;
When I ups with his heels, and smothers his
     squeals
   In the scum of the boiling broth.

"And I eat that cook in a week or less,
   And—as I eating be
The last of his chops, why I almost drops,
   For a wessel in sight I see.

  .   .   .   .   .   .

"And I never grieve, and I never smile,
   And I never larf nor play,
But I sit and croak, and a single joke
   I have—which is to say:

" Oh, I am a cook and a captain bold,
    And the mate of the *Nancy* brig,
And a bo'sun tight, and a midshipmite,
    And the crew of the captain's gig! "

W. S. GILBERT

THE BALLAD OF THE *CLAMPHERDOWN*

This was originally written for the *St. James's Gazette* as a deliberate skit on a letter by a correspondent who seemed to believe that Naval warfare of the future would be conducted on the old Nelsonic battle lines, including boarding, etc. By some accident it was treated from the first as a serious contribution—was, even, if I remember right, set to music as a Cantata. I never explained this till now.—*Rudyard Kipling*.

It was our warship *Clampherdown*
    Would sweep the Channel clean,
Wherefore she kept her hatches close
When the merry Channel chops arose,
    To save the bleached marine.

She had one bow-gun of a hundred ton,
    And a great stern-gun beside;
They dipped their noses deep in the sea,
They racked their stays and stanchions free
    In the wash of the wind-whipped tide.

It was our warship *Clampherdown*
    Fell in with a cruiser light
That carried the dainty Hotchkiss gun
And a pair o' heels wherewith to run
    From the grip of a close-fought fight.

She opened fire at seven miles—
   As ye shoot at a bobbing cork—
And once she fired and twice she fired,
Till the bow-gun drooped like a lily tired
   That lolls upon the stalk.

" Captain, the bow-gun melts apace,
   The deck-beams break below,
'Twere well to rest for an hour or twain,
And botch the shattered plates again."
   And he answered, " Make it so."

She opened fire within the mile—
   As ye shoot at the flying duck—
And the great stern-gun shot fair and true,
With the heave of the ship, to the stainless blue,
   And the great stern-turret stuck.

" Captain, the turret fills with steam,
   The feed-pipes burst below—
You can hear the hiss of the helpless ram,
You can hear the twisted runners jam."
   And he answered, " Turn and go! "

It was our warship *Clampherdown*,
   And grimly did she roll;
Swung round to take the cruiser's fire
As the White Whale faces the Thresher's ire
   When they war by the frozen Pole.

" Captain, the shells are falling fast,
   And faster still fall we;
And it is not meet for English stock
To bide in the heart of an eight-day clock
   The death they cannot see."

"Lie down, lie down, my bold A.B.,
  We drift upon her beam;
We dare not ram, for she can run;
And dare ye fire another gun,
  And die in the peeling steam?"

It was our warship *Clampherdown*
  That carried an armour-belt;
But fifty feet at stern and bow
Lay bare as the paunch of the purser's sow,
  To the hail of the Nordenfeldt.

"Captain, they hack us through and through;
  The chilled steel bolts are swift!
We have emptied the bunkers in open sea,
Their shrapnel bursts where our coal should be,"
  And he answered, "Let her drift."

It was our warship *Clampherdown*,
  Swung round upon the tide,
Her two dumb guns glared south and north,
And the blood and the bubbling steam ran forth,
  And she ground the cruiser's side.

"Captain, they cry, the fight is done,
  They bid you send your sword."
And he answered, "Grapple her stern and bow.
They have asked for the steel. They shall have
    it now;
  Out cutlasses and board!"

It was our warship *Clampherdown*,
  Spewed up four hundred men;

And the scalded stokers yelped delight
As they rolled in the waist and heard the fight,
   Stamp o'er their steel-walled pen.

They cleared the cruiser end to end,
   From conning-tower to hold.
They fought as they fought in Nelson's fleet;
They were stripped to the waist, they were bare
      to the feet,
   As it was in the days of old.

It was the sinking *Clampherdown*
   Heaved up her battered side—
And carried a million pounds in steel,
To the cod and the corpse-fed conger-eel,
   And the scour of the Channel tide.

It was the crew of the *Clampherdown*
   Stood out to sweep the sea,
On a cruiser won from an ancient foe,
As it was in the days of long ago,
   And as it still shall be.

RUDYARD KIPLING

JOCK O' THE SIDE

I

Now Liddesdale has ridden a raid,
   But I wat they had better hae staid at hame;
For Michael o' Winfield he is dead,
   And Jock o' the Side is prisoner ta'en.

II

To Sybill o' the Side the tidings came;
  By the waterside there as she ran
She took her kirtle by the hem
  And fast to Mangerton she's gane.

III

Then up and spoke her Lord Mangerton—
  "What news, what news, my sister to me?"—
"Bad news, bad news! My Michael is slain;
  And they ha'e taken my son Johnie."

IV

The lords they wrang their fingers white,
  Ladyes did pull themsells by the hair,
Crying "Alas and well-a-day!
  For Jock o' the Side we'll never see mair!"

V

—"Ne'er fear, sister Sybill," quo' Mangerton;
  "I have yokes of ousen, eighty and three;
My barns, my byres, and my faulds, a' weil fill'd,
  I'll part wi' them a' ere Johnie shall dee.

VI

"Three men I'll send to set him free,
  Well harness'd a' wi' the best o' steel;
The English louns may hear, and drie
  The weight o' their braid-swords to feel.

VII

"The Laird's Jock ane, the Laird's Wat twa,
  O Hobbie Noble, thou ane maun be!
Thy coat is blue, thou hast been true,
  Since England banish'd thee, to me."

VIII

Now Hobbie was an English man,
  In Bewcastle dale was bred and born;
But his misdeeds they were sae great,
  They banish'd him ne'er to return.

IX

Lord Mangerton them orders gave,
  "Your horses the wrang way maun be shod,
Like gentlemen ye mauna seem,
  But look like corn-caugers[1] ga'en the road.

X

"Your armour gude ye mauna shaw,
  Nor yet appear like men o' war;
As country lads be a' array'd,
  Wi' branks[2] and brecham[3] on each mare."

XI

Their horses are the wrang way shod,
  And Hobbie has mounted his grey sae fine;
Wat on his auld horse, Jock on his bey,
  And on they rode for the water of Tyne.

XII

But when they came to Cholerton ford
  They lighted down by the light o' the moon,
And a tree they cut, wi' nogs on each side,
  To climb up the wa' of Newcastle toun.

[1] Corn hucksters.   [2] Wooden halter.   [3] Straw collar.

XIII

But when they cam to Newcastle toun,
　And down were alighted at the wa',
They fand thair tree three ells ower laigh,[1]
　They fand their stick baith short and sma'.

XIV

Then up spake the Laird's ain Jock:
　"There's naething for't; the gates we maun
　　force."—
But when they cam the gate until,
　The porter withstood baith men and horse.

XV

His neck in twa the Armstrangs wrang;
　Wi' fute or hand he ne'er play'd pa!
His life and his keys at anes they ha'e ta'en,
　And cast the body ahint the wa'.

XVI

Now sune they reach Newcastle jail,
　And to the prisoner thus they call:
"Sleeps thou, wakes thou, Jock o' the Side,
　Or art thou weary of thy thrall?"

XVII

Jock answers thus, wi' dolefu' tone:
　"Aft, aft I wake—I seldom sleep:
But whae's this kens my name sae weel,
　And thus to mese[2] my waes does seek?"—

---

[1] Low.　　　　　[2] Soothe.

149

XVIII

Then out and spak the gude Laird's Jock,
  "Now fear ye na, my billie,"[1] quo' he;
"For here are the Laird's Jock, the Laird's Wat,
  And Hobbie Noble to set thee free."—

XIX

"Now haud thy tongue, my gude Laird's Jock,
  For ever, alas! this canna be;
For if a' Liddesdale were here the night,
  The morn's the day that I maun dee.

XX

"Full fifteen stane o' Spanish iron,
  They hae laid a' right sair on me;
Wi' locks and keys I am fast bound
  In this dungeon dark and dreirie."

XXI

"Fear ye na that," quo' the Laird's Jock;
  "A faint heart ne'er wan a fair ladie;
Work thou within, we'll work without,
  And I'll be sworn we'll set thee free."

XXII

The first strong door that they cam at,
  They loosèd it without a key;
The next chain'd door that they cam at,
  They garr'd it a' to flinders flee.

XXIII

The prisoner now upon his back
  The Laird's Jock has gotten up fu' hie;

[1] Pal.

And, airns and a', down the tolbooth[1] stair,
  Wi' nae sma' speed and joy brings he.

XXIV

"Now, Jock, my man," quo' Hobbie Noble,
  "Some o' his weight ye may lay on me."—
"I wat weel no!" quo' the Laird's ain Jock,
  "I count him lighter than a flee."

XXV

Sae out at the gates they a' are gane,
  The prisoner's set on horseback hie;
And now wi' speed they've ta'en the gate,
  While ilk ane jokes fu' wantonlie:

XXVI

"O Jock! sae winsomely ye sit,
  Wi' baith your feet upon ae side;
Sae weel ye're harneist, and sae trig,
  In troth ye sit like ony bride!"

XXVII

The night, tho' wat, they did na mind,
  But hied them on full merrilie,
Until they came to Cholerton brae,
  Where the water ran like mountains hie.

XXVIII

But when they came to Cholerton ford,
  There they met with an auld man;
Says—"Honest man, will the water ride?
  Tell us in hast, if that ye can."—

[1] Gaol.

XXIX

" I wat weel no," quo' the gude auld man;
  " I hae lived here thretty years and three;
Nor man nor horse can go ower Tyne,
  Except it were a horse of tree."—

XXX

Then out and spoke the Laird's saft Wat,
  The greatest coward in the companie:
" Now halt, now halt! we need na try't;
  The day is come we a' maun die! "—

XXXI

" Puir faint-hearted thief! " cried the Laird's
    ain Jock,
  " There'll nae man die but him that's fie;[1]
I'll guide ye a' right safely thro';
  Lift ye the pris'ner on ahint me."

XXXII

Wi' that the water they hae ta'en,
  By ane's and twa's they a' swam thro';
" Here are we a' safe," quo' the Laird's Jock,
  " And, puir faint Wat, what think ye now? "

XXXIII

They scarce the other brae had won,
  When twenty men they saw pursue;
Frae Newcastle toun they had been sent,
  A' English lads baith stout and true.

XXXIV

But when the Land-sergeant the water saw,
  " It winna ride, my lads," says he;

[1] Fey, doomed.

Then cried aloud—" The prisoner take,
　　But leave the fetters, I pray, to me! "

XXXV

" I wat weel no," quo' the Laird's ain Jock,
　　" I'll keep them, shoon to my mare to be:
My gude bay mare—for I am sure,
　　She has bought them a' right dear frae thee."—

XXXVI

Sae now they are on to Liddesdale,
　　E'en as fast as they could them hie;
The prisoner is brought to his ain fireside,
　　And there o' his airns they mak him free.

XXXVII

" Now, Jock, my billie," quo' a' the three,
　　" The day is comed thou was to die;
But thou's as weel at thy ain ingle-side,
　　Now sitting, I think, 'twixt thee and me."

ANONYMOUS

THE TASKS OF PSYCHE

(From " Eros and Psyche ")

She took her then aside, and bade her heed
A heap of grains piled high upon the floor,
Millet and mustard, hemp and poppy seed,
And fern-bloom's undistinguishable spore,
All kinds of pulse, of grasses, and of spice,
Clover and linseed, rape, and corn, and rice,
Dodder, and sesame, and many more.

" Sort me these seeds," she said; " it now is night,
I will return at morning; if I find
That thou hast separated all aright,
Each grain from other grain after its kind,
And set them in unmingled heaps apart,
Then shall thy wish be granted to thine heart."
Whereat she turn'd and closed the door behind.

A single lamp there stood beside the heap,
And shed thereon its mocking golden light;
Such as might tempt the weary eye to sleep
Rather than prick the nerve of taskèd sight.
Yet Psyche, not to fail for lack of zeal,
With good will sat her down to her ordeal,
Sorting the larger seeds as best she might.

When lo! upon the wall, a shadow passed
Of doubtful shape, across the chamber dim
Moving with speed: and seeing nought that cast
The shade, she bent her down the flame to trim;
And there the beast itself, a little ant,
Climb'd up in compass of the lustre scant,
Upon the bowl of oil ran round the rim.

Smiling to see the creature of her fear
So dwarf'd by truth, she watcht him where he crept,
For mere distraction telling in his ear
What straits she then was in, and telling wept.
Whereat he stood and trim'd his horns; but ere
Her tale was done resumed his manner scare,
Ran down, and on his way in darkness kept.

But she intent drew forth with dextrous hand
The larger seeds, or pushed the smaller back,

Or light from heavy with her breathing fanned.
When suddenly she saw the floor grow black,
And troops of ants flowing in noiseless train,
Moved to the hill of seeds, as o'er a plain
Armies approach a city for attack;

And gathering on the grain, began to strive
With grappling horns; and each from out the heap
His burden drew, and all their motion live
Struggled and slid upon the surface steep.
And Psyche wonder'd, watching them, to find
The creatures separated kind from kind:
Till dizzied with the sight she fell asleep.

And when she woke 'twas with the morning sound
Of Aphrodite's anger at the door,
Whom high amaze stayed backward, as she found
Her foe asleep with all her trouble o'er;
And round the room beheld, in order due,
The piles arranged distinct and sorted true,
Grain with grain, seed with seed, and spore with
        spore.

She fiercely cried, "Thou shalt not thus escape;
For to this marvel dar'st thou not pretend.
There is but one that could this order shape,
Demeter,[1]—but I knew her not thy friend.
Therefore another trial will I set,
In which she cannot aid thee or abet,
But thou thyself must bring it fair to end."

Thereon she sped her to the bounds of Thrace,
And set her by a river deep and wide,

---

[1] The Earth Goddess.

And said "To east beyond this stream, a race
Of golden-fleecèd sheep at pasture bide.
Go seek them out; and this thy task, to pull
But one lock for me of their precious wool
And give it in my hands at eventide:

This do and thou shalt have thy heart's desire."
Which said, she fled and left her by the stream:
And Psyche then, with courage still entire
Had plunged therein; but now of great esteem
Her life she rated, while it lent a spell
Wherein she yet might hope to quit her well,
And in one winning all her woes redeem.

There as she stood in doubt, a fluting voice
Rose from the flood, "Psyche, be not afraid
To hear a reed give tongue, for 'twas of choice
That I from mortal flesh a plant was made.
My name is Syrinx:[1] once from mighty Pan
Into the drowning river as I ran,
The change I begged my steps for ever stayed.

But for that change in many climes I live;
And Pan, my lover, who to me alone
Is true and does me honour, I forgive—
Nor, if I speak in sorrow, is't my own;
Rather for thee my voice I now uplift
To warn thee, plunge not in the river swift,
Nor seek the golden sheep to men unknown.

If thou should cross the stream, which may not be,
Thou couldst not climb upon the hanging rocks,
Nor ever, as the goddess bade thee, see

[1] A Greek word meaning a reed or pipe.

The pasture of the yellow-fleecèd flocks:
Or if thou could, their herded horns would gore
And slay thee on the crags, or thrust thee o'er
Ere thou couldst rob them of their golden locks.

The goddess means thy death. But I can show
How thy obedience yet may thwart her will.
At noon the golden flocks descend below,
Leaving the scented herbage of the hill,
And where the shelving banks to shallows fall,
Drink at the rippling waters one and all,
Nor back return till they have drawn their fill.

I will command a thorn bush, that it stoop
Over some ram that steppeth by in peace,
And him in all its prickles firmly coop,
Making thee seizure of his golden fleece;
So without peril of his angry horns
Shalt thou be quit: for he upon the thorns
Must leave his ransom ere he win release."

Then Psyche thanked her for her kind befriending,
And hid among the rushes looking east;
And when noon came she saw the flock descending
Out of the hills; and, lo! one golden beast
Caught in a thorn bush; and the mighty brute
Struggled and tore from its twisted root
Into the stream, or e'er he was released.

And when they watered were and gone, the breeze
Floated the freighted thorn where Psyche lay:
Whence she unhooked the golden wool at ease,

And back to heaven for passage swift gan pray.
And Hermes,[1] who was sent to be her guide
If so she lived, came down at eventide,
And bore her thither ere the close of day.

ROBERT BRIDGES

THE DAEMON LOVER

" O where have you been, my long, long love,
    This long seven years and more? "—
" O I'm come to seek my former vows
    Ye granted me before."—

" O hold your tongue of your former vows,
    For they will breed sad strife;
O hold your tongue of your former vows,
    For I am become a wife."

He turned him right and round about,
    And the tear blinded his ee;
" I wad never hae trodden on Irish ground,
    If it had not been for thee.

I might hae had a king's daughter,
    Far, far beyond the sea;
I might have had a king's daughter,
    Had it not been for love o' thee."

" If ye might have had a king's daughter,
    Yer sell ye had to blame;
Ye might have taken the king's daughter,
    For ye kend that I was nane!

[1] The messenger of the gods.

158

If I was to leave my husband dear,
  And my two babes also,
O what have you to take me to,
  If with you I should go? "

" I hae seven ships upon the sea;
  The eighth brought me to land,
With four and twenty bold mariners,
  And music on every hand."

She has taken up her two little babes,
  Kissed them both cheek and chin;
" O fare ye well, my own two babes,
  For I'll never see you again."

She set her foot upon the ship;
  No mariners could she behold,
But the sails were o' the taffetie,
  And the masts o' the beaten gold.

She had not sailed a league, a league,
  A league but barely three,
When dismal grew his countenance,
  And drumlie[1] grew his ee.

They had not sailed a league, a league,
  A league but barely three,
Until she espied his cloven foot,
  And she wept right bitterly.

" O hold your tongue of your weeping," says he,
  " Of your weeping now let me be;
I will show you how the lilies grow
  On the banks of Italy! "—

[1] Gloomy.

159

"O what hills are yon, yon pleasant hills,
    That the sun shines sweetly on?"
"O yon are the hills of heaven," he said,
    "Where you will never win."—

"O whaten a mountain is yon," she said,
    "All so dreary wi' frost and snow?"
"O yon is the mountain of hell," he cried,
    "Where you and I will go."

He strack the tap-mast wi' his hand,
    The fore-mast wi' his knee;
And he brake that gallant ship in twain,
    And sank her in the sea.

ANONYMOUS

REYNARD IN FLIGHT

(From "Reynard the Fox")

The fox heard hounds get on to his line,
And again the terror went down his spine;
Again the back of his neck felt cold,
From the sense of the hound's teeth taking hold.
But his legs were rested, his heart was good,
He had breath to gallop to Mourne End Wood;
It was four miles more, but an earth at end,
So he put on pace down the Rood Hill Bend.

Down the great grass slope which the oak-trees dot,
With a swerve to the right from the keeper's cot,
Over High Clench Brook in its channel deep,
To the grass beyond, where he ran to sheep.

The sheep formed line like a troop of horse,
They swerved, as he passed, to front his course.
From behind, as he ran, a cry arose:
" See the sheep there. Watch them. There he
    goes! "

He ran the sheep that their smell might check
The hounds from his scent and save his neck,
But in two fields more he was made aware
That the hounds still ran; Tom had viewed him
    there.

Still, as he ran, his pads slipped back,
All his strength seemed to draw the pack,
The trees drew over him dark like Norns,
He was over the ditch and at the thorns.

He thrust at the thorns, which would not yield;
He leaped, but fell, in sight of the field.
The hounds went wild as they saw him fall,
The fence stood stiff like a Bucks flint wall.

He gathered himself for a new attempt;
His life before was an old dream dreamt,
All that he was was a blown fox quaking,
Jumping at thorns too stiff for breaking,
While over the grass in crowd, in cry,
Came the grip teeth grinning to make him die,
The eyes intense, dull, smouldering red,
The fell like a ruff round each keen head,
The pace like fire, and scarlet men
Galloping, yelling, " Yooi, eat him, then! "

He gathered himself, he leaped, he reached
The top of the hedge like a fish-boat beached.

He steadied a second and then leaped down
To the dark of the wood where bright things drown.

He swerved, sharp right, under young green firs.
Robin called on the Dane with spurs.
He cried, " Come, Dansey; if God's not good,
We shall change our fox in this Mourne End
  Wood."
Tom cried back as he charged like spate,
" Mine can't jump that, I must ride to gate."
Robin answered, " I'm going at him.
I'll kill that fox, if it kills me, drat him!
We'll kill in covert. Gerr on, now, Dane."
He gripped him tight and he made it plain,
He slowed him down till he almost stood,
While his hounds went crash into Mourne End
  Wood.

Like a dainty dancer, with footing nice
The Dane turned side for a leap in twice.
He cleared the ditch to the red clay bank,
He rose at the fence as his quarters sank,
He barged the fence as the bank gave way,
And down he came in a fall of clay.

Robin jumped off him and gasped for breath
He said, " That's lost him as sure as death.
They've overrun him. Come up, the Dane.
We'll kill him yet, if we ride to Spain."

He scrambled up to his horse's back,
He thrust through cover, he called his pack;
He cheered them on till they made it good,
Where the fox had swerved inside the wood.

The fox knew well as he ran the dark,
That headlong hounds were past their mark;
They had missed his swerve and had overrun,
But their devilish play was not yet done.

For a minute he ran and heard no sound,
Then a whimper came from a questing hound,
Then a "This way, beauties," and then "Leu
  Leu,"
The floating laugh of the horn that blew.
Then the cry again, and the crash and rattle
Of the shrubs burst back as they ran to battle,
Till the wood behind seemed risen from root,
Crying and crashing, to give pursuit,
Till trees seemed hounds and the air seemed cry,
And the earth so far that he needs but die,
Die where he reeled in the woodland dim,
With a hound's white grips in the spine of him
For one more burst he could spurt, and then
Wait for the teeth, and the wrench, and men.

He made his spurt for the Mourne End rocks.
The air blew rank with the taint of fox;
The yews gave way to a greener space
Of great stones strewn in a grassy place.
And there was his earth at the great grey shoulder,
Sunk in the ground, of a granite boulder.
A dry, deep burrow with rocky roof,
Proof against crowbars, terrier-proof,
Life to the dying, rest for bones.

The earth was stopped; it was filled with stones.

JOHN MASEFIELD

BALDER'S FUNERAL

(From " Balder Dead ")

But now the sun had pass'd the height of Heaven,
And soon had all that day been spent in wail;
But then the Father[1] of the ages said: —
   " Ye Gods, there well may be too much of wail!
Bring now the gather'd wood to Balder's ship;
Heap on the deck the logs, and build the pyre."
   But when the Gods and Heroes heard, they brought
The wood to Balder's ship, and built a pile,
Full the deck's breadth, and lofty; then the corpse
Of Balder on the highest top they laid,
With Nanna[2] on his right, and on his left
Hoder, his brother, whom his own hand slew.
And they set jars of wine and oil to lean
Against the bodies, and stuck torches near,
Splinters of pine-wood, soak'd with turpentine;
And brought his arms and gold, and all his stuff,
And slew the dogs who at his table fed,
And his horse, Balder's horse, whom most he loved,
And placed them on the pyre, and Odin threw
A last choice gift thereon, his golden ring.

The mast they fixt, and hoisted up the sails,
Then they put fire to the wood; and Thor[3]
Set his stout shoulder hard against the stern
To push the ship through the thick sand;—sparks
   flew

[1] Odin.
[2] Balder's wife.
[3] Son of Odin and god of war.

From the deep trench she plough'd, so strong a God
Furrow'd it; and the water gurgled in.
And the ship floated on the waves, and rock'd.
But in the hills a strong east-wind arose,
And came down moaning to the sea; first squalls
Ran black o'er the sea's face, then steady rush'd
The breeze, and fill'd the sails, and blew the fire.
And wreathed in smoke the ship stood out to sea.
Soon with a roaring rose the mighty fire,
And the pile crackled; and between the logs
Sharp quivering tongues of flame shot out, and leapt,
Curling and darting, higher, until they lick'd
The summit of the pile, the dead, the mast,
And ate the shrivelling sails; but still the ship
Drove on, ablaze above her hull with fire.
And the Gods stood upon the beach, and gazed.
And while they gazed, the sun went lurid down
Into the smoke-wrapt sea, and night came on.
Then the wind fell, with night, and there was calm;
But through the dark they watch'd the burning ship
Still carried o'er the distant waters on,
Farther and farther, like an eye of fire.
And long, in the far dark, blazed Balder's pile;
But fainter, as the stars rose high, it flared,
The bodies were consumed, ash choked the pile,
And as, in a decaying winter-fire,
A charr'd log, falling, makes a shower of sparks—

So with a shower of sparks the pile fell in,
Reddening the sea around; and all was dark.

MATTHEW ARNOLD

THE VOYAGE OF MAELDUNE

(FOUNDED ON AN IRISH LEGEND A.D. 700)

I

I was the chief of the race—he had stricken my father
dead—

But I gather'd my fellows together, I swore I would
strike off his head.

Each of them look'd like a king, and was noble in birth
as in worth,

And each of them boasted he sprang from the oldest
race upon earth.

Each was as brave in the fight as the bravest hero of
song,

And each of them liefer had died than have done one
another a wrong.

He lived on an isle in the ocean—we sail'd on a Friday
morn—

He that had slain my father the day before I was born.

II

And we came to the isle in the ocean, and there on the
shore was he.

But a sudden blast blew us out and away thro' a boundless sea.

III

And we came to the Silent Isle that we never had touch'd
at before,

Where a silent ocean always broke on a silent shore,

And the brooks glitter'd on in the light without sound,
and the long waterfalls

Pour'd in a thunderless plunge to the base of the mountain walls,

And the poplar and cypress unshaken by storm flourish'd up beyond sight,

And the pine shot aloft from the crag to an unbelievable height,

And high in the heaven above it there flicker'd a songless lark,

And the cock couldn't crow, and the bull couldn't low, and the dog couldn't bark.

And round it we went, and thro' it, but never a murmur, a breath—

It was all of it fair as life, it was all of it quiet as death,

And we hated the beautiful Isle, for whenever we strove to speak

Our voices were thinner and fainter than any flittermouse-shriek;

And the men that were mighty of tongue and could raise such a battle-cry

That a hundred who heard it would rush on a thousand lances and die—

O they to be dumb'd by the charm!—so fluster'd with anger were they

They almost fell on each other; but after we sail'd away.

IV

And we came to the Isle of Shouting, we landed, a score of wild birds

Cried from the topmost summit with human voices and words;

Once in an hour they cried, and whenever their voices peal'd

The steer fell down at the plow and the harvest died
    from the field,
And the men dropt dead in the valleys and half of the
    cattle went lame,
And the roof sank in on the hearth, and the dwelling
    broke into flame;
And the shouting of these wild birds ran into the hearts
    of my crew,
Till they shouted along with the shouting and seized
    one another and slew;
But I drew them the one from the other; I saw that we
    could not stay,
And we left the dead to the birds and we sail'd with our
    wounded away.

v

And we came to the Isle of Flowers: their breath met us
    out on the seas,
For the Spring and the middle Summer sat each on the
    lap of the breeze;
And the red passion-flower to the cliffs, and the dark-
    blue clematis, clung,
And starr'd with a myriad blossom the long convolvulus
    hung;
And the topmost spire of the mountain was lilies in lieu
    of snow,
And the lilies like glaciers winded down, running out
    below
Thro' the fire of the tulip and poppy, the blaze of gorse,
    and the blush
Of millions of roses that sprang without leaf or a thorn
    from the bush;

And the whole isle-side flashing down from the peak
   without ever a tree

Swept like a torrent of gems from the sky to the blue of
   the sea;

And we roll'd upon capes of crocus and vaunted our kith
   and our kin,

And we wallow'd in beds of lilies, and chanted the triumph of Finn,

Till each like a golden image was pollen'd from head to
   feet

And each was as dry as a cricket, with thirst in the
   middle-day heat.

Blossom and blossom, and promise of blossom, but never
   a fruit!

And we hated the Flowering Isle, as we hated the isle
   that was mute,

And we tore up the flowers by the million and flung them
   in bight and bay,

And we left but a naked rock, and in anger we sail'd
   away.

VI

And we came to the Isle of Fruits: all round from the
   cliffs and the capes,

Purple or amber, dangled a hundred fathom of grapes,

And the warm melon lay like a little sun on the tawny
   sand,

And the fig ran up from the beach and rioted over the
   land,

And the mountain arose like a jewell'd throne thro' the
   fragrant air,

Glowing with all-colour'd plums and with golden masses
   of pear,

And the crimson and scarlet of berries that flamed upon
    bine and vine,
But in every berry and fruit was the poisonous pleasure
    of wine;
And the peak of the mountain was apples, the hugest
    that ever were seen,
And they prest, as they grew, on each other, with hardly
    a leaflet between,
And all of them redder than rosiest health or than utter
    est shame,
And setting, when Even descended, the very sunset
    aflame;
And we stay'd three days, and we gorged and we mad
    den'd, till every one drew
His sword on his fellow to slay him, and ever they struck
    and they slew;
And myself, I had eaten but sparely, and fought till I
    sunder'd the fray,
Then I bad them remember my father's death, and we
    sail'd away.

VII

And we came to the Isle of Fire: we were lured by the
    light from afar,
For the peak sent up one league of fire to the Northern
    Star;
Lured by the glare and blare, but scarcely could stand
    upright,
For the whole isle shudder'd and shook like a man in a
    mortal affright;
We were giddy besides with the fruits we had gorged
    and so crazed that at last

There were some leap'd into the fire; and away we sail'd,
  and we past
Over that undersea isle, where the water is clearer than
  air:
Down we look'd: what a garden! O bliss, what a Para-
  dise there!
Towers of a happier time, low down in a rainbow deep
Silent palaces, quiet fields of eternal sleep!
And three of the gentlest and best of my people, whate'er
  I could say,
Plunged head down in the sea, and the Paradise trembled
  away.

VIII

And we came to the Bounteous Isle, where the heavens
  lean low on the land,
And ever at dawn from the cloud glitter'd o'er us a sunbright hand,
Then it open'd and dropt at the side of each man, as he
  rose from his rest,
Bread enough for his need till the labourless day dipt
  under the West;
And we wander'd about it and thro' it. O never was time
  so good!
And we sang of the triumphs of Finn, and the boast of
  our ancient blood,
And we gazed at the wandering wave as we sat by the
  gurgle of springs,
And we chanted the songs of the Bards and the glories
  of fairy kings;
But at length we began to be weary, to sigh, and to
  stretch and yawn,

Till we hated the Bounteous Isle and the sunbright hand
    of the dawn,

For there was not an enemy near, but the whole green
    Isle was our own,

And we took to playing at ball, and we took to throwing
    the stone,

And we took to playing at battle, but that was a perilous
    play,

For the passion of battle was in us, we slew and we sail'd
    away.

IX

And we past to the Isle of Witches and heard their
    musical cry—

" Come to us, O come, come " in the stormy red of a sky

Dashing the fires and the shadows of dawn on the
    beautiful shapes,

For a wild witch naked as heaven stood on each of the
    loftiest capes,

And a hundred ranged on the rock like white sea-birds
    in a row,

And a hundred gamboll'd and pranced on the wrecks in
    the sand below,

And a hundred splash'd from the ledges, and bosom'd
    the burst of the spray,

But I knew we should fall on each other, and hastily
    sail'd away.

X

And we came in an evil time to the Isle of the Double
    Towers,

One was of smooth-cut stone, one carved all over with
    flowers,

But an earthquake always moved in the hollows under the dells,

And they shock'd on each other and butted each other with clashing of bells,

And the days flew out of the Towers and jangled and wrangled in vain,

And the clash and boom of the bells rang into the heart and the brain,

Till the passion of battle was on us, and all took sides with the Towers,

There were some for the clean-cut stone, there were more for the carven flowers,

And the wrathful thunder of God peal'd over us all the day,

For the one half slew the other, and after we sail'd away.

XI

And we came to the Isle of a Saint who had sail'd with St. Brendan of yore,

He had lived ever since on the Isle and his winters were fifteen score,

And his voice was low as from other worlds, and his eyes were sweet,

And his white hair sank to his heels and his white beard fell to his feet,

And he spake to me, " O Maeldune, let be this purpose of thine!

Remember the words of the Lord when He told us 'Vengeance is Mine!'

His fathers have slain thy fathers in war or in single strife,

173

Thy fathers have slain his fathers, each taken a life fo
    a life,
Thy father had slain his father, how long shall th
    murder last?
Go back to the Isle of Finn and suffer the Past to b
    Past."
And we kiss'd the fringe of his beard and we pray'd as w
    heard him pray,
And the Holy man he assoil'd us, and sadly we sail'
    away.

XII

And we came to the Isle we were blown from, and ther
    on the shore was he,
The man that had slain my father. I saw him and le
    him be.
O weary was I of the travel, the trouble, the strife an
    the sin,
When I landed again, with a tithe of my men, on th
    Isle of Finn.

LORD TENNYSOI

THE CAPTAIN

(A LEGEND OF THE NAVY)

He that only rules by terror
    Doeth grievous wrong.
Deep as Hell I count his error.
    Let him hear my song.
Brave the Captain was: the seamen
    Make a gallant crew,
Gallant sons of English freemen,
    Sailors bold and true.
But they hated his oppression,

Stern he was and rash;
So for every light transgression
  Doom'd them to the lash.
Day by day more harsh and cruel
  Seemed the Captain's mood.
Secret wrath like smother'd fuel
  Burnt in each man's blood.
Yet he hoped to purchase glory,
  Hoped to make the name
Of his vessel great in story,
  Wheresoe'er he came.
So they past by capes and islands,
  Many a harbour-mouth,
Sailing under palmy highlands—
  Far within the South.
On a day when they were going
  O'er the lone expanse,
In the north, her canvas flowing,
  Rose a ship of France.
Then the Captain's colour heighten'd
  Joyful came his speech:
But a cloudy gladness lighten'd
  In the eyes of each.
"Chase," he said: the ship flew forward
  And the wind did blow;
Stately, lightly, went she Norward,
  Till she near'd the foe.
Then they look'd at him they hated,
  Had what they desired:
Mute with folded arms they waited—
  Not a gun was fired.
But they heard the foeman's thunder

Roaring out their doom;
All the air was torn in sunder,
   Crashing went the boom,
Spars were splinter'd, decks were shatter'd,
   Bullets fell like rain;
Over mast and deck were scatter'd
   Blood and brains of men.
Spars were splinter'd; decks were broken:
   Every mother's son—
Down they dropt—no word was spoken—
   Each beside his gun.
On the decks as they were lying,
   Were their faces grim.
In their blood, as they lay dying,
   Did they smile on him.
Those, in whom he had reliance
   For his noble name,
With one smile of still defiance
   Sold him unto shame.
Shame and wrath his heart confounded,
   Pale he turn'd and red,
Till himself was deadly wounded
   Falling on the dead.
Dismal error! fearful slaughter!
   Years have wander'd by,
Side by side beneath the water
   Crew and Captain lie;
There the sunlit ocean tosses
   O'er them mouldering,
And the lonely seabird crosses
   With one waft of the wing.

LORD TENNYSON

ARMSTRONG, MARTIN. Born 1882. He has written novels, short stories and works of criticism as well as poetry.

ARNOLD, MATTHEW. 1822-1888. The son of the famous headmaster of Rugby. He was Professor of Poetry at Oxford and he was also an inspector of schools. He is perhaps more famous as a critic than as a poet, yet he wrote some poems of striking beauty. You should read *Balder* from which the extract printed here has been taken. Then read *Sohrab and Rustum*.

AYTOUN, WILLIAM EDMONDSTOUNE. 1813-1865. One of Aytoun's ancestors, Sir Robert Aytoun (1570-1638), is supposed to have written the original poem on which Robert Burns based his *Auld Lang Syne*. Look in the library for Aytoun's *Lays of the Scottish Cavaliers*.

BARHAM, RICHARD HARRIS. 1788-1845. Barham was educated at St. Paul's School and at Oxford. Read his *Ingoldsby Legends*.

BINYON, LAURENCE. Born 1869. Formerly the Keeper of Prints and Drawings in the British Museum. Binyon is not only a poet and playwright, but also an expert authority on Chinese art.

BRIDGES, ROBERT. 1844-1930. Bridges began his career as a doctor, but later he decided to devote himself to poetry. His reputation was made by his *Shorter Poems*. In 1913 he was appointed Poet Laureate and in 1929 he published his great philosophical poem, *The Testament of Beauty*. His love of the English countryside is reflected in many of his poems, such as *November, Nightingales* and *The Winnowers*.

BROWNING, ROBERT. 1812-1889. The son of a clerk in the Bank of England. Browning's first poem, *Pauline*, was published in 1833. In 1846 he married Elizabeth Barrett, and because of her poor health he took her to Italy where he remained until her death in 1861. Their romance is the subject of the well-known play *The Barretts of Wimpole Street*. Browning's virile and rugged style has always attracted readers. He has been described very aptly as the poet of human nature and, especially in his " dramatic mono-logues ", his power of revealing character is very great. You will enjoy all Browning's narrative poems. Read *How they brought the Good News from Ghent to Aix* and the *Cavalier Tunes*.

BYRON, GEORGE GORDON, LORD. 1788-1824. Byron had an unhappy childhood. When he went to Harrow he played cricket in spite of the great disability of his club foot. His poems are very popular on the Continent and particularly in Greece where he met his death when fighting on the side of the Greeks against the Turks. Read *The Destruction of Sennacherib* and *Childe Harold's Pilgrimage*.

COWPER, WILLIAM. 1731-1800. Cowper was the son of the rector of Great Berkhampstead. He was called to the Bar in 1754, but fits of depression caused him to give up the idea of legal work. His best known poems include *The Task*, a delightful description of rural scenes and the pleasures of country life, *John Gilpin* and such well-known hymns as *Hark, my soul! It is the Lord* and *God Moves in a Mysterious Way*.

DE LA MARE, WALTER. Born 1873. His *Songs of Childhood* was published under the pen-name of Walter Ramal. He has since written many volumes of poetry, including *Peacock Pie*. Here are a few poems by De la Mare that you will find in *The Poet's Way* and *The Poet's Company*—*Silver, All That's Past, Goliath, The Linnet*.

DRAYTON, MICHAEL. 1563-1631. Drayton was born in Warwickshire and wrote many historical and religious poems. You should read *A Fine Day, To the Virginia Voyage* and *Nimphidia*.

GIBSON, WILFRID WILSON. Born 1878. In the war of 1914-1918 Gibson served in the ranks. He is one of the best of the narrative poets of our time. Read *The Ice Cart* and *The Tiger*.

GILBERT, SIR WILLIAM SCHWENCK. 1836-1911. Served as an officer in the militia and later became a clerk in the Education Department. He collaborated with Sir Arthur Sullivan in a very popular series of comic operas, such as *The Mikado, The Gondoliers*, etc. If you enjoy humorous verse you should read *Bab Ballads*.

KIPLING, RUDYARD. 1865-1936. Kipling was born in Bombay and spent the early years of his childhood in India. His short stories and patriotic poems won great popularity. He also wrote *Kim, The Light That Failed* and the *Jungle* stories. In *Stalky and Co.* he gives an account of his schooldays in England.

LONGFELLOW, WILLIAM WADSWORTH. 1807-1882. A prolific American poet whose numerous volumes of poetry were widely read on both sides of the Atlantic. Among the best known of his poems are: *The Wreck of the Hesperus, The Village Blacksmith* and *Hiawatha*.

MARRYAT, FREDERICK. 1792-1848. A captain in the Royal Navy whose early life at sea was crowded with stirring adventure. He is chiefly famous for his popular stories of sea life, such as *Mr. Midshipman Easy, Peter Simple*. Other tales most boys still enjoy are *The Settlers in Canada* and *Masterman Ready*. Christopher Lloyd has written a fascinating life of Marryat in which this gallant sailor's early life is described faithfully. When you read it you will realize why Marryat's sea stories are so true to life.

MASEFIELD, JOHN. Born 1878. Masefield fell in love with the sea when a boy and ran away to join a ship. His early experiences, like Marryat's, have helped him to paint vivid word pictures of life at sea in prose and verse. Yet, though a sailor, he is also, like so many of our greatest poets, a lover of the English countryside, as you will realize when you read *Reynard the Fox*. In 1930 Masefield succeeded Robert Bridges as Poet Laureate. There are many of Masefield's poems you will enjoy: *Cargoes, The Tewkesbury Road, The Wild Duck* and that delightful narrative poem *Dauber*.

NOYES, ALFRED. Born 1880. In 1914 Noyes was appointed Professor of Modern English Literature at Princeton University in U.S.A. One of his best known poems is *The Torchbearers*. You will like the other *Tales of the Mermaid Tavern* if you have enjoyed *A Knight of the Ocean-sea*.

PRAED, WINTHROP MACKWORTH. 1802-1839. Praed was educated at Eton and Trinity College, Cambridge. He became a Member of Parliament after being called to the Bar. Although he wrote some serious poetry he is remembered to-day for his narrative and humorous verse.

RENNELL, OF RODD, LORD. The poem in this volume, which tells the story of an expedition led by the Earl of Essex in the reign of Charles I, has been taken from the author's *Ballads of the Fleet*, a title no doubt borrowed from Lord Tennyson's sub-title to *The Revenge*. You should make a point of reading the other ballads Lord Rennell of Rodd has written.

RIEU, E. V. Born 1887. The author of *Cuckoo Calling* and other volumes of verse. His *Musical At Home* and *Sir Smasham Uppe* will appeal to you if you like *The Whale*.

ROSSETTI, DANTE GABRIEL. 1828-1882. The son of an Italian patriot who came to England in 1824. His most popular poems include *The Blessed Damozel, Rose Mary, The White Ship*. Many of his poems were written by way of commentary on his pictures, for Rossetti was also a celebrated painter.

SOUTHEY, ROBERT. 1774-1843. Southey was expelled from Westminster School in the days when flogging was prevalent, for he had the impudence to write an essay on that subject! His *Life of Nelson* is still widely read and so are his popular poems, *The Battle of Blenheim, The Inchcape Rock,* and *The Well of St. Keyne*.

STEVENSON, ROBERT LOUIS. 1850-1894. Lung trouble sent Stevenson abroad in his youth and later, in 1888, he settled in Samoa where he temporarily recovered his health; yet in spite of his handicap of ill-health he won great popularity as a poet, a novelist and an essayist. Among his writings are *A Child's Garden of Verses, Treasure Island, Kidnapped, Travels with a Donkey*. When you have read these you will need no further encouragement to search for his other writings.

TENNYSON, ALFRED, LORD. 1809-1892. Tennyson was born at Somersby where his father was rector. In 1850 he succeeded Wordsworth as Poet Laureate. When you have read a number of his poems you will become aware of his simplicity of style which along with the beauty of his melodious verse has placed him in an eminent position among the poets of the Victorian age. In one sense he can be regarded as complementary to Browning, from whom he differs so considerably in his mode of expression. Read *Ulysses*, *The Lotus Eaters*, and *Idylls of the King*.

WHITTIER, JOHN GREENLEAF. 1807-1892. Another American poet. His parents were Quakers and he lived with them in an ancient oak farmhouse in Massachusetts, built by one of his Puritan ancestors. Whittier, like Robert Burns, was at one time a farmer's boy, and it was Burns' verses that aroused and developed his own love of poetry. Later, he became a popular poet himself.

INDEX OF AUTHORS

INDEX OF AUTHORS